Jet

Butterworths Gem Books
Edited by Peter G. Read

Amber
Helen Fraquet

Beryl
John Sinkankas and Peter G. Read

Garnet
John D. Rouse

Jet
Helen Muller

Pearls: natural, cultured and imitation
Alexander E. Farn

Quartz
Michael O'Donoghue

In preparation

Corundum
Richard W. Hughes

Diamond
Roy V. Huddlestone

Opals
P. J. Darragh

Topaz
D. B. Hoover

Butterworths Gem Books

Jet

Helen Muller

Butterworths
London Boston Durban Singapore Sydney Toronto Wellington

First published 1987

© **Butterworths & Co (Publishers) Ltd. 1987**

British Library Cataloguing in Publication Data
Muller, Helen
    Jet.—(Butterworths gem books)
    1. Jet (Precious stone)
    I. Title
    553.8'7   QE394.J4
    ISBN 0-408-03110-7

Library of Congress Cataloging in Publication Data
Muller, Helen
    Jet.

    (Butterworths gem books)
    Bibliography: p.
    Includes index.
    1. Jet (Precious stone)   I. Title.   II. Series.
    QE394.J46M85   1987   553.8'7   86-26338
    ISBN 0-408-03110-7

Typeset by Scribe Design, Gillingham, Kent
Printed in Great Britain by Butler & Tanner Ltd, Frome and London

Preface

In this, the first book to be written on jet, I have collected and correlated the scattered pieces of information which hitherto have been the only records of this much-neglected gemstone. Such information has come mainly from learned journals of geology and archaeology or popular magazines, very little from books on jewellery or gemmology. Many of the details are the result of personal interviews with jet workers and their families in the UK and abroad.

The important Whitby jet industry has never been documented, and no previous account has dealt with the designs of the master craftsmen who were the artists of the industry and who are no longer here to reveal their secrets.

I hope that this introduction to this fine gem will encourage others in the fields of chemistry, physics, social history or art to research further into its nature and history and enlarge our knowledge of Britain's native gemstone.

Acknowledgements

I would like to acknowledge the invaluable help of Katy and John Muller whose fluent Spanish and German respectively were essential in the study of the jet of these two countries. Thanks are also due to the following: Bryan Barker, Ms P. Beswick, Pierre M. Cantou, G. Dürr, Mrs A. Kildale-Robinson, Mrs B. Lyth, Ms J. Mann, J.S. Owen, Ramon Requeixo Rebon, T. Roe, Jose Filgueira Valverde and to many others in Whitby, Germany and Spain.

Photographic credits

Grateful acknowledgement is also due to the following for providing photographs reproduced in this book: Simon Pentellow of the Photographic Section of the University of Leeds Audio Visual Services for Figures 1.1, 1.3, 4.14, 4.21, 4.22, 4.28, 4.34, 5.2, 5.4, 5.6, 5.10, 5.13, 5.14, 5.18, 5.20, 5.21, 5.23, 5.25, 5.31, 5.32, 5.34, 5.36, 5.38, 7.4, 7.6, 7.10, 7.11 and colour plates 1 and 2; Stella Mayes Reed for Figures 1.4, 2.2, 4.1, 4.2, 4.3, 4.4, 4.5, 4.6, 4.11, 4.12, 4.24, 4.27, 4.30, 4.32, 5.1, 5.3, 5.5, 5.7, 5.8, 5.9, 5.11, 5.15, 5.16, 5.17, 5.22, 5.24, 5.27, 5.28, 5.29, 5.30,

5.37, 6.23, 6.27, 7.2, 7.3, 7.7, 7.8, 7.9, 7.12 and 7.13; H. G. Muller for Figures 2.3 and 2.5; I. Aisbitt for Figure 2.8; John Owen for Figures 2.4, 2.7, 2.9 and 7.1; the National Museum of Antiquities of Scotland for Figures 3.1 and 6.17; the Yorkshire Museum for Figure 3.3; Bergen University Historical Museum for Figure 3.6; Rotunda Museum, Scarborough Borough Council, Department of Tourism and Amenities for Figures 3.7 and 4.5b; Michael Wrigley for Figures 4.8, 4.9 and 4.10; Sutcliffe Gallery, Whitby for Figures 4.16, 4.20 and 4.25; York Castle Museum for Figures 4.18 and 5.26b; Mrs B. Lyth for Figures 4.26, 4.29 and 4.31; Prof. Dr. K.D. Adam for Figure 6.1; Rheinisches Bildarchiv Köln for Figures 6.2, 6.3, 6.4, 6.5 and 6.6; Städisches Museum Schwäbisch Gmünd im Prediger for Figures 6.7, 6.8, 6.9 and 6.10; Germanisches National Museum Nürnberg for Figure 6.13; Museum of Pontevedra for Figures 6.14, 6.15, 6.16 and 6.18; Kunsthistorisches Museum, Vienna, for Figure 6.19; and the University of Arizona Press for Figure 6.25.

Contents

PROFILE: SUMMARY OF CONSTANTS AND CHARACTERISTICS

Crystal system	Amorphous
Chemical composition	Organic. Carboniferous, with traces of mineral elements such as aluminium, silicon and sulphur. Contains 12–19% mineral oil
Optical character	Opaque
RI	1.64–1.68
DR	None
Dispersion	None
Specific gravity	1.3–1.4
Hardness	2.5–4.0
Colour	Black
Lustre	Velvety
Fracture	Conchoidal
UV and X-ray luminescence	None
Other properties	Shows frictional electricity
Varieties	Hard jet and soft jet
Streak	Dark brown
Occurrence	France, Germany, Spain, UK, USA and USSR

ERRATA

The following photographs were incorrectly credited, and should be attributed as follows.
Figs. 3.5, 3.6, 4.23, 4.33, 7.4, 7.6, 7.10 and 7.14, and Plates 3, 4, 5, 6, 7 and 8: to Stella Mayes Reed; Fig. 3.7: to Bergen University Historical Museum, Norway; Fig. 3.8: to Scarborough Borough Council, Department of Tourism and Amenities; Fig. 4.15a to Sutcliffe Gallery, Whitby; Figs. 4.16, 4.20 and 4.25: to Whitby Museum; Fig. 7.1: to Dorset Natural History and Archaeological Society; Fig 7.2: to John Owen; Figs. 7.5, 7.7 and 7.12, and Plates 1, 2 and 9: to Simon Pentellow.

Page 40: Legend for Fig 4.12 (b) missing; should read: James Ainsley's advertisement in *Kelly's Directory* of 1880, when he was already combining his jet business with that of a feed merchant.
Page 67: Fig. 5.1 — Number and legend missing. Legend should read: A large brooch of the mid 19th century bearing the cross, heart and anchor which represented faith, hope and charity. Width 63 mm. Total length 158mm.
Page 78: Fig. 5.16 — Legend should refer to Fig. 7.12 not 7.10.
Page 79: Fig. 5.17 — The top brooch is the mourning brooch and the lower the token of affection.

Chapter 1

General description

Black, forsooth; coal-black, as jet.

Shakespeare

Introduction

Few people know much about jet. Many have never even heard of it. Those that have, know only that it is black and associate it with mourning jewellery. This is not surprising, for no books have ever been written on the subject, and very little research has been conducted into its chemical or physical nature. The only information available about jet is to be found in a few magazine articles and some papers in learned geological journals.

Probably no other gemstone has suffered such variations of fortune as jet. In the course of one century it swung from being the height of fashion to being completely shunned and unwanted.

Yet jet is a gemstone with a history as old and as long as any other known gem, a history that goes back to mankind's earliest use of decorative materials. Furthermore, throughout its thousands of years of use as a gem it was known as a magical jewel, a bringer of good fortune and a protecter against all evil.

There have been three great ages of jet in the United Kingdom: the Bronze Age, the Roman era and the 19th century. It reached its zenith in Victorian England and it was in this period that jet lost its aura of magic and acquired its fatal association with mourning.

Strangely, jet appears to have suffered a similar fate in other parts of the world. In those countries where it is found and used it has also had periods of popularity, only to be followed by times in which it has faded away to become unknown and ignored.

But wherever jet is found there is no doubt that it was one of the first materials to be used to make articles for personal adornment, and it has always carried with it an aura of magic and good fortune.

Description

The name jet is synonymous with the colour black. The phrase 'as black as jet' has been used in literature at least since the 11th century. The gem's colour is intense and never fades. Its lustre has been described as waxy or velvety. When polished,

Figure 1.1 Left: A piece of jet showing typical conchoidal fracture. *Middle:* Mined jet showing the skin or spar. *Right:* A piece of sea-washed jet as it is washed up on the shore, the skin has been removed and the corners rounded by the action of the waves

the lustre is sufficiently bright for pieces of jet to have been used as mirrors in medieval times.

Jet is tough and homogeneous, but its hardness is low on Mohs' scale, reaching only 4 in the best quality. It is therefore easily scratched or damaged, but is very suitable for carving. When broken it shows a lustrous conchoidal fracture (*Figure 1.1*).

If rubbed vigorously on wool or silk, jet acquires an electric charge that enables it to attract small pieces of straw or paper. Its low specific gravity (1.3–1.4) contributed greatly to its use in large pieces of jewellery. Its optical properties are of little importance since it is opaque. An indistinct line at about 1.66 may be seen on a refractometer, but this is of little use as a diagnostic feature.

Jet is a poor conductor of heat and feels warm to the touch – another pleasant feature when it is used in jewellery.

The chemical composition of jet is similar to that of brown coal or lignite, being carbonaceous with traces of mineral elements. A chemical analysis gives the following results:

Carbon 75.2%	Hydrogen 7.0%	Nitrogen 0.7%
Sulphur 4.6%	Oxygen 12.5%	

It also contains traces of silicon, potassium, calcium, iron, copper and aluminium.

Very little work has been done on the chemical properties of jet, although some attempts have been made to determine the provenance of samples of jet from different countries. For example, X-ray emission spectroscopy has been used to compare the proportions of certain of its specific constituent elements (Muller, 1980). Although only a limited number of specimens of foreign jet was available for testing, the results showed an interesting relationship between the three mineral elements, aluminium, silicon and sulphur. Generally, jet from Whitby in Yorkshire contained a relatively high proportion of aluminium, while Spanish jet contained more sulphur (*Figure 1.2*).

There has been much confusion in the past between jet and its near relatives. For instance, many 19th century archaeologists were unable to distinguish between jet, lignite, cannel coal and shale. Most black grave goods were labelled 'jet', and many museums today have collections from the Bronze Age or from Roman times in which no distinction is made between any of these materials (Pollard *et al.*, 1981). Furthermore, many Scottish Bronze Age barrows have yielded jet jewellery, but there is no way of determining at present whether the jet came from the Whitby area or from the small deposits which were found in parts of Scotland.

It would be a great advantage if a fairly simple method of discriminating between these similar substances could be found. Such a test could then also be used to

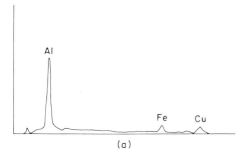

(a)

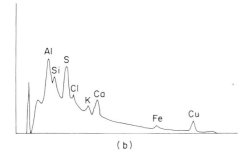

(b)

Figure 1.2 Graphs showing the X-ray emission spectrum of the internal surface of Whitby jet and of Spanish jet. The high proportion of aluminium in the Whitby sample (a) and of sulphur in the Spanish sample (b) can be seen

establish the provenance of a given sample. This would be an invaluable aid to archaeologists and to museums.

Because of its high volatile content, jet burns readily with a sooty blue/green flame, and was indeed used as a fuel before the jet industry was established.

Jet produces a brown streak when rubbed on unglazed porcelain. The depth of colour of the streak gives some indication of the quality of the jet: the harder the jet, the lighter the streak.

Varieties

Two varieties of jet are recognized and are given the rather misleading names of hard and soft jet. In fact, both may have the same hardness on Mohs' scale, but hard jet is tough and durable and can be worked and polished and retain its shape and lustre for centuries. These qualities can be seen in the many Bronze Age jet artifacts which are still in existence.

Soft jet is brittle and will not stand up to rapid changes of temperature. It thus has a tendency to crack and split a short time after it has been worked (*Figure 1.3*). Hard and soft jet are at first indistinguishable by sight, and this fact led to much disappointment when the inferior type was made into ornaments which subsequently cracked.

The two forms in which jet is found are known as plank jet and cored jet (see Chapter 2).

When jet is mined it has a blueish/grey skin, known as spar, which has to be removed before the jet can be worked (*Figure 1.1*). The spar is a thin layer of the surrounding shale and often shows the impressions of fossils (*Figure 1.4*). Jet that has been washed up on the seashore is known as 'sea washed jet'. The tumbling

Figure 1.3 Beads made from soft jet showing the typical cracking and splitting which it undergoes after being worked. The diameter of the largest bead is 27 mm

action of the waves has removed the spar and given the outer layer a rough polish. Any sharp edges have also been rubbed off which gives the pieces a rounded outline (*Figure 1.1*). However, jet cannot be tumbled like the harder pebbles found on the beach.

Occurrence

Because it has not always been possible in the past to distinguish between true jet and its near relatives, reports of jet being found in various locations may not always be completely accurate.

Figure 1.4 Rough jet showing the imprint of ammonite fossils

A type of jet was said to have come from Russia and from Turkey, which was the ancient source known to the Greeks and Romans as Lycia. However, there are no modern references to these two sources. The occurrence of jet has also been reported from China, but there is no information about its detailed locality there. The *Minerals Yearbook* for 1939 states that considerable amounts of jet were produced in the province of Kompong-Thom in Cambodia, but here again there is no up-to-date reference to this source.

A good supply of jet was obtainable in Germany from ancient times until the 17th century when interest in its use faded. It was found in the Poseidon slate of the Jurassic period, and was probably formed under similar geological conditions to those of the Yorkshire area. The location of the source was in south Germany in the Swabian and Frankish Alps particularly around Balingen, Reutlingen and Göppingen.

In France, as in Germany, there appears to have been a source of jet which was utilized in the Middle Ages. It was found in the Department of Aude in Bains, in Peyrax and at Sainte Colombe. That source appears to have run out in the 19th century.

Jet today is found in Spain, in Asturias and Aragon, and in the USA in Colorado and Utah.

In the United Kingdom small amounts of jet were found in the past in Scotland, but the main source today is in the North York Moors National Park area of North Yorkshire. The area is roughly bounded by the A19 road to the west, the A171 to the north, the A170 to the south and the sea to the east. Two well known walks cover the area, the Cleveland Way from Filey up the coast to Saltburn and inland to Helmsley, and the Lyke Wake Walk from Osmotherley to Ravenscar.

Origin of the name

The ancient Greeks and Romans obtained their jet from Gages, which is the name of both a town and river in Lycia in Asia Minor. Lycia was on the Mediterranean coast of what is now Turkey. From Gages was derived jet's original name of gagates. This was the name used by the Romans and is the origin of the modern

German name Gagat, although in medieval times the Germans also called it Augstein. Both the French and English words are also derived from the Latin. The French call it jaiet or jyet. The old English name was geate or geat, and from this it became jeat. (There are references to workers called jeaters in the literature of 17th century England.) Finally the word was shortened to jet.

A dictionary of Old English gives 1387 as the date at which the word jet was first used, but many variations are found in the literature throughout the Medieval period, including in 1502 the word Gette.

The Irish Gaelic word for jet is gaing, which still shows traces of the Latin root. But in Welsh the word is muchydd, which is entirely original. Articles of jet have turned up in Welsh burial sites, and it seems quite possible that there was a source in Wales in ancient times. This would explain its having a purely Welsh name unassociated with any Latin derivation. In Spain too the word for jet, azabache, has a quite independent origin (see Chapter 6).

References

MULLER, H., 'A note on the composition of jet', *The Journal of Gemmology,* **XVII,** No. 1 (1980)

POLLARD, A. M., BUSSELL, G. D. and BAIRD, D. C., (1981), 'The analytical investigation of early bronze age jet and jet-like material from the Devizes museum', *Archaeometry,* **23,** 139–167 (1981)

Chapter 2
Geology and mining

Her hair,
Adown her shoulders loosely lay displayed
And in her jetty curls, ten thousand cupids played.

Prior

The origin of jet

Although it is now generally accepted that jet is a fossilized wood, a very heated discussion about its origin took place throughout the 19th century. In the early part of that century, the ligneous nature of jet was accepted, but once the industry started to expand and the miners and the workmen took an interest in the nature of the rocks in which jet was found, new theories were advanced and many arguments ensued.

It was pointed out that the beds in which the jet occurred were highly bituminous, and one author wrote: 'The segregation of the bitumen in the intervals of the shales, which, allowing to a certain extent the access of air, has hardened into jet, a process which may undoubtedly be now going on' and he concludes 'there seems to be no reason whatever for connecting it with wood' (Tate and Blake,1876). J. G. Lyth, one of the last craftsmen, was convinced that jet was the fossilized sap of a primitive tree because of its similarity to amber and because when working jet he came across stones embedded in it. It is not surprising that those who worked the jet and who were familiar with amber should see similarities between the two and deduce that they had similar origins. Both are easy to work, amorphous and above all show the ability to become electrically charged when rubbed. The ancient Romans called jet 'black amber'. In fact, they had only the one word for the two gems. The erroneous term black amber has been perpetuated to the present day. One author in the 19th century became so carried away with the idea that he dubbed jet 'Succinum nigrum' (Parkinson, 1811). At the time he could be forgiven, but there can be no excuse for the present-day use of such titles as 'The black amber of Whitby'. Worse still, a series of otherwise excellent articles about jet once appeared under the title 'The black turquoise of Whitby'.

There were therefore two theories of the origin of jet. One suggested that it was bituminous resin, the other that it was fossilized wood. A compromise was suggested in 1892. This proposed that jet was a pseudomorphic replacement of wood by bitumen (Fox–Strangways,1892). Seward in 1904 was the first to examine jet in microscopic section and showed that it was definitely derived from wood. The

Figure 2.1 Electron micrograph of jet showing the wood vessels (about ×2000)

Figure 2.2 A piece of rough jet showing the annual rings and the compression of the wood

fossil wood found in the Whitby Lias is a species of Araucaria (the monkey puzzle tree) but of a much larger size than those of the present day.

Recent work with an electron microscope (Muller,1980) clearly shows in even better detail the ligneous nature of jet. In (*Figure 2.1*) the tracheids can be seen clearly, and they show the spiral arrangement of the original cellulose fibrils.

In exceptionally fine specimens of rough jet the annual rings of the original wood can be distinguished (*Figure 2.2*), and in cored jet – a form of jet with a siliceous centre surrounded by a jet layer some 50–75 mm thick – the shape of the original branches can still be seen, together with knots and stem bases.

Jetonization

The method of formation of jet was described in the classic work of Hemingway in 1933. He showed that when the trees died and fell they began to dry up and crack and a little aerobic decomposition took place. During times of heavy rain and floods the trees would be swept away by rivers, being tumbled and abraded on the way. During their journey to the sea they were probably broken up and had their branches torn off. At times they might rest on sandbanks where grains of sand or small pebbles adhered to them. Eventually, the trees reached the sea where they became water-logged and sank into the black mud of the sea-floor.

Figure 2.3 The shale on a jet spoil heap which has weathered out into thin layers each of which is thought to represent an annual fall of debris in the Lias sea

Over millions of years dead plants and animals and other sediment settled on the wood. This annual fall of detritus can now be seen in the laminations of the shale on the old jet spoil heaps (*Figure 2.3*). The weight of the mud and of the overlying water exerted a great pressure which flattened the wood (*Figure 2.2*).

At the depth at which the wood lay there was no oxygen, and so anaerobic decomposition took place from the outside inwards. The tissues gradually changed to jet, which spread inwards along the medullary rays. In some wood the centre of the stem became silicified before jetonization and in this way cored jet was formed.

More commonly, jet is found in thin seams no more than 25–50 mm thick which have a plano-convex outline in cross section. Here the wood is compressed and the original shape is lost. This is known as plank jet, which is always found lying in the bedding plane of the surrounding shale.

Microscopic sections of hard jet show the medullary rays buckled and the cells collapsed and replaced by organic compounds. In soft jet the cells are uncompressed and are filled with a yellow organic derivative. This difference in structure accounts for the greater durability of hard jet and the cracking of soft jet after working. It is probable that soft jet was formed in fresh water and therefore under more aerobic conditions.

We can therefore say that hard jet is wood which has been compressed so as to eliminate almost all cell cavities. It has been exposed over millions of years to great pressure, to chemical changes which have taken place under strongly reducing conditions and to anaerobic decomposition. These conditions existed in the Lias sea of what is now North Yorkshire. Similar conditions existed in South Germany during the Jurassic period, and it is likely that the same process there gave rise to the German deposits (Marshall,1974; Gad, Catt and le Riche,1969).

Geology

In the area of the North York Moors National Park (*Figure 2.4*), which roughly corresponds to what was once the Jurassic sea, the coastline consists of very steep cliffs, many up to 75 m high. In these cliffs the geological succession can be seen very clearly, and the jet rock of the Upper Lias period may be exposed anywhere from Ravenscar in the south to Saltburn in the north. From Ravenscar the jet outcrops in the cliffs as far as Homerell Hole about 1.6 km north of Robin Hood's

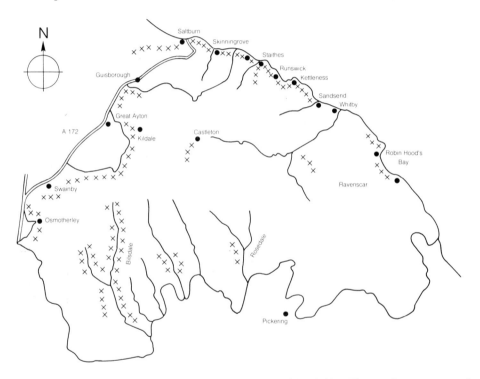

Figure 2.4 The positions (X) of 19th century jet mines in North Yorkshire. The area shown corresponds to the area of the North York Moors National Park and to the part of the country covered by the sea in the Jurassic period (after J. S. Owen)

Bay. At this point the jet shales dip below sea level and reappear at Sandsend north of Whitby. Continuing towards Saltburn, the shales are visible in the cliffs for most of the way towards Runswick. Near Hob Holes they are again lost until just north of Port Mulgrave. From there they can be followed almost all the way to Saltburn.

Turning inland jet is found along the north faces of Upleatham and Eston Hills. South of Guisborough extensive workings have been made into the north face of

Guisborough Moor, then following the escarpment to the west via Roseberry Topping to Kildale. Southwards the line runs through Battersby, Ingelby Moor and Greenhow Moor to the top of Clay Bank. Further south jet is found along Bilsdale, Tripsdale, Tarn Hole and Raisdale. The furthest point west is Osmotherley (which is named after the mother of Oswy, King of Northumbria, see Chapter 4). Then on the southern border jet is found in the beautiful valleys of Westerdale, Bransdale, Rosedale and Littlebeck.

On the ordnance survey map there is an ancient British settlement marked at Roseberry Topping, and here shallow pits can be seen where it is believed that the ancient Britons and later the Romans may have dug for jet.

Many of these picturesque hills and valleys bear testimony to the industry of the old jet miners, for the unsightly spoil heaps are barren and remain so today to scar the landscape (*Figure 2.5*).

Figure 2.5 The spoil heaps from old jet mines on Carleton Bank near Great Ayton, North Yorkshire. The path is part of the Lyke Wake walk

The Jurassic rocks are divided into the Upper, Middle and Lower Jurassic. The Lower Jurassic is further sub-divided into the Upper, Middle and Lower Lias Regions and it is in the Upper Lias that jet is found (*Figure 2.6*).

Around Whitby the Upper Lias of the Lower Jurassic consists of the following strata. At the top is the dogger, a layer of ferruginous rock which in the 19th century was worked as an ironstone and known as the Top Seam of Cleveland. Below the dogger are the alum shales which were mined extensively in the past for the alum industry. Next comes a layer of hard shales with ironstone concretions and below them the bituminous shales which have a high mineral oil content. This oil, which is a product of the decomposition of marine life, has never been

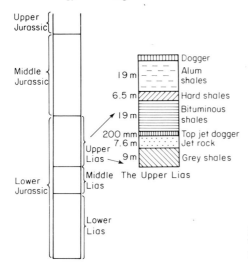

Figure 2.6 The geological succession in North Yorkshire and the position of the jet rock in the Upper Lias

commercially exploited. Separating the bituminous shales from the jet rock is a band of hard limestone, about 200 mm thick, called the top jet dogger. This weathers out into large discoidal concretions up to 3.6 m in diameter, known locally as mermaid's dining tables.

The jet rock is a group of black laminated shales 7.6 m thick, from the upper 3 m of which the best hard jet is obtained. The jet occurs at random in the shale in pockets which the miners called seams. The jet shale when freshly broken has a characteristic oily smell and is said to contain about 19 gallons per ton of sulphurous oil (Hemingway, 1958).

For the miners searching for jet it was obviously important that they should be able to identify the jet rock proper without having any extensive knowledge of geology. In this they were helped by two features with which they were quite familiar. The first was the large circular flat boulders of limestone, the mermaid's dining tables. Once a layer of these was found they knew that jet might be found directly below. Furthermore if the miners tunnelled into the shale, the tables above made a strong solid roof for their adits or shafts. The second feature was that the shales of the Lower Jurassic were rich in fossils. Ichthyosaurs and plesiosaurs have been found there, but more abundant were the ammonites. These 'snake stones' as they were called locally were particularly useful because each geological stratum was characterized by one particular species. The ammonite found in the jet rock was *Harpoceras exeratum* (*Figure 1.4*). The miners were quite familiar with the different types of fossils which were not only good indicators for the jet, but which were also collected and incorporated into the ornaments and jewellery made from the jet. Iron pyrites and zinc blende were also associated with the jet, although neither were of any commercial value.

As might be supposed from its method of formation the jet is distributed randomly among the jet shales. Finding pieces of sufficient size was very much a hit and miss operation. The plank jet is usually only a few centimetres thick, and 30 to

60 cm is a good length. The largest recorded piece of plank jet ever found was 1.93 m long, 114–140 mm wide and 38 mm thick. It weighed 5 kg.

Soft jet is found in the overlying bituminous shales and those of the Middle Jurassic.

Mining

Pieces of jet may be picked up on the beaches all along the east coast of Yorkshire. Some of this will come from the area where the Lias rocks lie below the sea between Homerell Hole and Sandsend, part of which form the dangerous Whitby rocks. Other pieces may have been washed out of the cliffs at high tide and thrown up again on the beach. Beachcombing was probably the source of jet from prehistoric times until the 19th century. As the Whitby jet industry grew and the demand for jet exceeded this simple method of supply new techniques were developed in the search for the raw material.

Cliff falls, particularly after severe storms, had often exposed new seams, so it was obviously an improvement on nature to encourage the falls by digging into the cliffs. Evidence of this still exists in the form of caves along the shore line particularly around Kettleness (*Figure 2.7*). Dynamite was not normally used to get at the jet because it would damage it, but there is a report that a few men did blast the exposed shale at low tide below the cliffs on the north side of Sandsend

Figure 2.7 The shore at Kettleness where evidence of Victorian jet mining can be seen in numerous man-made caves cut into the rock. Running horizontally across the picture on the left is the top jet dogger

(Sandsend Ness). Some of the drill holes they made can still be seen. A certain Moses Thompson, 'Old Mosey Thompson', was killed when he went back to examine a misfired shot. It was not a misfire, and it blew up in his face, killing him on the spot.

Where the jet seams were too high to be worked from the beach, a new and dangerous occupation known as 'dessing' was developed. This meant that a man was lowered by rope from the cliff top to reach the seam. It often proved fatal.

Finally it was realized that jet could be found inland and this was when the true mining began. John Owen, who has made a life-long study of mining in this area, has estimated that it did not begin until 1840 (Owen, 1975). By this time the miners had discovered that the jet shales inland, which had been exposed on a sloping hillside, had weathered and were much easier to work than those on the sea cliffs.

Mining was a fairly simple operation. It consisted of digging a 'drift', or tunnel, into the hillside using a pick and shovel. If jet was found, a series of parallel drifts would be driven straight into the hillside, each being about 1.8 m high by 0.9 to 1.2 m wide. At regular intervals other headings would be driven at right angles to the drifts leaving pillars of rock at the junctions to support the roof. As the miners worked inwards the discarded shale was removed in a wheelbarrow and tipped down the hillside. If the mine was fairly extensive a row of planks with a central groove was laid down to guide the wheelbarrow. Since the mines seldom extended more than 90 m into the hillside it was never necessary to use timber supports.

The miners used simple tools; a pick drawn out into a sharp point and a shovel were all that were needed. Candles were used for lighting.

When the initial tunnel had been excavated as far as possible it was said to have come to the 'face'; then a systematic reworking of the roof would take place. The miners hewed down the roof right up to the level of the top jet dogger (*Figure 2.8*). The shale was left behind as they retreated, so that the original floor of the mine was raised by many feet, leaving only enough space for the miners to work.

Searching for jet in this way was a haphazard occupation. Many tales are told of those who worked their claim for weeks and found nothing, only for someone to come after them to discover a large and valuable seam.

Jet mining does not appear to have been an organized industry. Usually one or two men worked together, and the largest number of men to be employed in one mine seems to have been twelve. Many miners were part-timers whose main employment was in the local iron-stone mines, on farms or as sailors home from the sea. In order to search for jet it was necessary to pay rent to the landowner (*Figure 2.9*). This was either assessed on the number of miners employed or sometimes a royalty had to be paid on all the jet found. In 1851 a rent of £20 per annum was paid for one mine provided that no more than four workmen were employed (Owen, 1975). Much of the land in the Runswick, Kettleness and Sandsend area belonged to the Marquis of Normanby, and the Marchioness did much to popularize the wearing of jet at court.

The landowners were not overly enthusiastic about jet mining on their land. The ugly spoil heaps marred the countryside, while an extensive mine could undercut the ground like a large rabbit warren and so make it useless for cultivation. Thus mining was usually only permitted on land unsuitable for agriculture. An old jet

Figure 2.8 Inside an old inland jet mine. The roof has been pulled down, raising the floor so that it is only possible to crawl along

---

HEADS OF AGREEMENT

for permitting the working of Jet in Cliffs at Staithes in the County of York, on Property belonging to Mr. Arthur Willis, of Cliff Farm, Staithes, Yorks.

1. The term to be One Year from the

2. The rent to be on a sharing basis, and we the undersigned hereby agree to render to Mr Arthur Willis punctually on the First day of every month full particulars of the weight of all Jet got, and of all sales thereof during the preceding month, and such other particulars respecting the working of the Jet as the said Arthur Willis may require, AND to pay to him, the said Arthur Willis, One equal third part or share of the gross proceeds of sale of such Jet.

3. The workings to be commenced at a place to be mutually agreed upon, the drifting to be carried on in the most approved manner so as to cause no damage to surface, especially on farm lands.

4. Should the place decided upon prove unremunerative, we the Lessees to be allowed to proceed to some other part of the Cliff belonging to the said Arthur Willis by duly notifying him of such intention, the consent of the latter to be obtained and the old place of working made secure before the new working is commenced.

5. Any damage to surface to be made good ; any damage to stock or otherwise resulting from the workings authorised under these Heads of Agreement to be satisfactorily compensated for by us the Lessees, and in the event of any dispute the amount of claim to be settled by arbitration in the usual way.

6. It is also mutually agreed by the Lessees that the Lessor, the said Arthur Willis, is not and will not be responsible for any liability under the Workmen's Compensation Act, 1906, whatsoever through any accident or accidents which may occur to one or any one of the Lessees during the term of this Lease

We agree to enter into this Agreement for the working of Jet upon the terms and conditions hereinbefore set forth.

As Witness our hands this   day of   1921.

Figure 2.9 An example of the type of agreement entered into by the jet miners with the land owners

mine was rediscovered in recent years when a farmer found that his lost cow had fallen into it.

It appears that wages for the miners were fairly low. In 1873 at the height of the demand for jet ornaments, miners were earning 24–26 shillings (£1.25) a week (Bower, 1873). This was for an eight-hour day, six days a week. About 200–300 men were engaged in the mining industry at that time.

The value of the rough jet varied considerably according to the demands of the industry and the quality of the jet. In 1873 a figure of 4 to 21 shillings (20p–£1.05) per pound weight is quoted. This is a large variation, but large unflawed pieces were rare and would command a very high price.

As the demand for jet jewellery declined, so did the need for mining as sufficient jet could again be found in the cliffs and on the beaches. Mining probably ceased altogether in the late 1920s. However, the scars of the industry still remain on the Cleveland hills. A drive along the A172 from Osmotherley to Saltburn shows a line of shale heaps following the jet rock stratum along the hills to the south of the road. Some of these spoil heaps are a salmon-pink colour where they have burnt. Spontaneous combustion is always possible because of the relatively large quantity of oil in the shale.

The old mines are mostly worked out now, but they can be visited with an experienced guide if permission is obtained from the owner of the land. They are historically interesting, but for anyone wishing to look for jet it is better to search the old spoil heaps.

There is undoubtedly a considerable quantity of jet still left in the North Yorkshire hills, but it is unlikely ever to be mined again. In spite of the recent resurgence of interest in jet working, the jet found on the beaches is sufficient to supply the needs of the craftsmen of today.

References

BOWER, J. A., 'Whitby jet and its manufacture', *Journal of the Society of Arts*, **XXII** (1873)

FOX–STRANGWAYS, C., *The Jurassic rocks of Britain: Vol. 1 Memoirs of the Geological Survey Yorkshire*, HMSO (1892)

GAD, M. A., CATT, J. A. AND LE RICHE, H. H., 'Geochemistry of the Whitbian (Upper Lias) sediments of the Yorkshire coast,' *Proceedings of the Yorkshire Geological Society*, Vol. 37, part 1, No. 5 (1969)

HEMINGWAY, J. E., 'Whitby jet and its relation to Upper Lias sedimentation in the Yorkshire Basin', PhD thesis, Leeds University (1933)

HEMINGWAY, J. E., 'The geology of the Whitby area,' Whitby Museum Publication (1958)

HEMINGWAY, J.E. AND RAYNOR, D. H. (eds.), *Geology and mineral resources of Yorkshire* Yorkshire Geological Society (1974)

LYTH, J. G., *Whitby jet, some questions and answers*, private publication (1957)

MARSHALL, C. E., 'The jet story', *The Australian Gemmologist* (1974)

MULLER, H., 'A note on the composition of jet', *Journal of Gemmology*, **XVII**, No. 1 (1980)

OWEN J. S., 'Jet mining in North East Yorkshire', *Cleveland Industrial Archaeologist*, No. 3, (1975)

PARKIN, C., 'On jet mining,' *Transactions of the Northern Engineering Institute of Mining and Mechanical Engineers*, Vol. 31 (1882)

PARKINSON, J., *The organic remains of a former world*, 3 vols, London (1811)

ROBINSON, P. C., 'A geological guide to the jet industry on the Yorkshire coast', *Scarborough and district Archaeological Society Transactions*, Vol. 1, No. 5 (1962)

SEWARD, A. C., *The Jurassic Flora*, British Museum Publication, Part II, London (1904)

TATE, R. J. AND BLAKE, F., *The Yorkshire Lias*, John van Voorst, London (1876)

Chapter 3

Jet in history

But her hair and her eyebrows,
Blacker were they than jet.

Mabinogion

Prehistoric use

During the Stone Age jet was used in Germany and France (see Chapter 6), but although Mesolithic and Neolithic settlements are known in Yorkshire there is no evidence that jet was used in Britain at that time. However, lack of evidence does not necessarily mean that the people of these settlements did not make any use of jet for their amulets or personal adornment. It is well known from other parts of the world that Stone-Age people employed many natural objects for these purposes, and jet would be an obvious choice for those living in Britain.

However, the use of jet became widespread in the Bronze Age, which began around 2700 BC. By this time the hunting and gathering way of life of the Stone Age had developed into a settled existence based on early methods of agriculture. Perhaps it is because these early farmers enjoyed a more settled life that we find decorative as well as useful grave goods amongst their possessions.

It is fortunate for the archaeologist that the Bronze Age people practised inhumation – burial in a grave – and that they marked their burial sites with large mounds of earth. These mounds varied in size and shape. The large rectangular structures, known as long barrows, usually mark a multiple grave site. The large or small round barrows are often, but not always, single graves. Finally single burials sometimes took place in a very small grave called a short cist. In all these burials grave goods were placed alongside the body.

Sometime between 2500 and 2000 BC a group of people from the Rhineland and the Low Countries settled in the eastern districts of Britain and spread inland as far as West Yorkshire in the north. They are known as the Beaker people because of their custom of interring distinctive pottery drinking cups with their dead. Flint scrapers, knives, arrowheads and decorative objects of jet have also been found in Beaker graves (*Figure 3.1*).

In Yorkshire there are many thousands of these Bronze Age barrows (Hawkes, 1976). Some are large, and others are very small and grouped together in 'cemeteries'. In Scotland too they occur in large numbers. At least 59 Scottish sites have yielded examples of jet jewellery, ranging from a single bead to elaborate necklaces (Morrison, 1979).

Figure 3.1 Reconstruction of a crescentic necklace of jet beads of the food vessel period with four spacer plates and two end plates (from a site in Poltalloch, Scotland)

The jet for this Bronze Age jewellery could have been found washed up on the beach, and its attractive glossy appearance would no doubt have appealed to these early craftsmen who would find it useful for the making of amulets. At first a simple piece, bored and strung on a thong, might have been used. However, once they realized that its appearance could be improved by polishing, they would have discovered its ability to attract to itself bits of chaff or straw. This electrostatic property would have seemed to be powerful magic, and would have enhanced the value of jet as a talisman and amulet, thus beginning its long career as a bringer of good fortune.

By about 1000 BC the beaker folk were gradually replaced by another wave of immigrants, the so-called Food Vessel people. The different design of pot found in their graves gives them both a different name and a later date (*Figure 3.2*). They also practised inhumation and their tombs have yielded jet jewellery. Towards the end of this period these people began to cremate their dead and to bury their ashes in urns in a short cist, but even then the grave goods accompanied the urn.

Many Bronze Age barrows were excavated in the 19th century and the list of jet objects found is long and varied. They range from very elaborate necklaces consisting of hundreds of beads to single beads, buttons, earrings, pendants and belt sliders. Jewellery was found with both male and female skeletons (Evans, 1897).

Although the greatest number of jet objects have come from Scotland, Yorkshire and Derbyshire, isolated finds have been made in the Wessex burials and as far away as Anglesey in North Wales. Whether or not the articles were made from what we now call Whitby jet cannot be proven until some method has been devised to ascertain the source of the jet.

In Scotland there were small deposits of jet in East Sutherland, Skye and Mull. However, none is known from Derbyshire. It appears (Raistrick, 1976) that these early people had quite well developed trade routes. Bronze axes were brought from Ireland and jet could have been traded for tin from the south of England. It should be pointed out, however, that not all objects excavated in the 19th century and

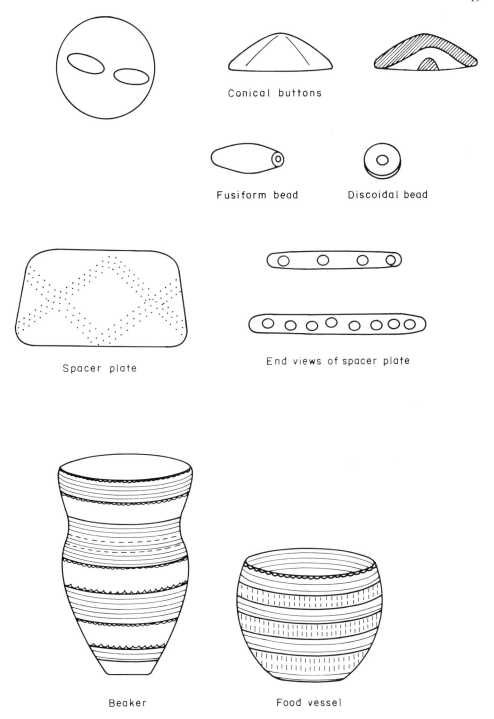

Conical buttons

Fusiform bead

Discoidal bead

Spacer plate

End views of spacer plate

Beaker

Food vessel

Figure 3.2 Line drawings of a beaker, food vessel, spacer plates and two ends of a spacer plate.

labelled jet, and which are now found in museums, are actually jet, because of the common confusion with lignite and shale.

The necklace found in Poltalloch in Scotland may be described as typical of the more elaborate crescentic necklaces found in many sites in Scotland, Yorkshire and Derbyshire (Craw, 1928). It is from the Food Vessel period, and was found in a cist together with a flint knife and some partially incinerated bones and teeth. It consists of 110 fusiform beads with four spacer plates, two end plates and a fastener. The reconstruction of the necklace shown in *Figure 3.1* may not be accurate. Authorities disagree about the threading of the beads in a net-like arrangement. Most consider that simple rows of beads are more likely, possibly up to ten in number.

Both end plates and spacer plates are decorated with a pointillé pattern of dots, and this is commonly found in many jet necklaces and also on amber necklaces of a similar age and type. The function of the spacer plates is to increase the number of rows of beads from 1 to 3, 3 to 5, 5 to 10, or some other combination such as 4 to 8 (as illustrated in *Figure 3.2*).

There is a uniformity of shape to these crescentic necklaces whether they come from Scotland or Yorkshire which suggests that they may have been based on the more expensive and rarer gold necklaces that have been found in Ireland and Wales. The jet necklaces bear a strong resemblance to these gold lunulae and it is possible that some of the larger ones may have been worn, not around the neck, but from shoulder to shoulder as was the Irish gold collar at present in the British Museum.

It is interesting that amber necklaces from the same period were of a similar shape and construction. The similar decoration on the spacer plates has already been mentioned. The size of some of these crescentic necklaces may be judged by one found more recently in Easter Essendy Farm, Perth, Scotland. Here there were six spacer plates increasing the rows of beads from 2 to 4, from 4 to 5 and from 5 to 10. Ninety-six fusiform beads were found, so the original must have been a truly impressive necklace (Thoms, 1980).

The other type of bead found in Bronze Age necklaces is a flat perforated disc. An example of this type is the necklace which was found in Calcais Wold in Yorkshire. This consisted of 573 of these disc shaped beads strung together side by side (Mortimer, 1905).

Bronze Age buttons were usually conical in shape being drilled from two points on the underside which met in a V (Evans, 1897). Most of the jet necklaces were fastened by a conical fastener perforated in a V as in the buttons. The Easter Essendy necklace is unusual in having a cylindrical fastener.

In North Derbyshire two working sites from the early Bronze Age have been found. They are high on the moors above Sheffield at Swine Sty and Totley Moor. At these sites flint and stone tools were found as well as a bronze 'pricker' together with rough and half worked shale and cannel coal.

From the study of these sites it has been possible to deduce how such elaborate jewellery was made. The jet was first trimmed along the bedding planes, probably using a flint knife. Then it was cut out into the rough shape of the object being made. The surface was ground down using fine sandstone and then a hole was made, either by gouging it out with a pricker or by using a simple twist drill tipped with a microlith or small worked flint. When shaping beads on a flat sandstone surface a groove would be rubbed into the sandstone. On the depth of that groove would depend the exact shape of the bead. Finally the articles were polished by using jet powder mixed with grease on a piece of leather or fleece. The fusiform beads were evidently drilled from both ends with amazing accuracy. The disc beads were probably produced by cutting a long cylindrical bead into thin sections. The pointillé patterns on the spacer plates could have been made with a small sharp flint or a bronze pricker (Beswick, 1975).

The Roman period

The ancient Romans obtained a supply of jet from Lycia (modern Turkey). This information is given in the 1st century AD by Pliny the Elder. In Chapter 34 of his Natural History he writes of jet:

> 'It is black, smooth, light and porous, differs but little from wood in appearance, is of a brittle texture and emits a disagreeable odour when rubbed. Marks made upon pottery with this stone cannot be effaced. When burnt, it gives out a sulphureous smell; and it is a singular fact, that the application of water ignites it, while that of oil quenches it. The fumes of it, burnt, keep serpents at a distance, and dispel hysterical affections: they detect a tendency also to epilepsy, and act as a test of virginity. A decoction of this stone in wine is curative of toothache; and in combination with wax, it is good for scrofula.'

Pliny's account, like many which followed it, is a strange mixture of observation, hearsay and superstition. His remark that jet differs but little from wood in appearance suggests that it might have been nearer to lignite than true jet. The observation that oil quenches and water ignites it must have been borrowed from some previous account since it has no basis of fact. The test for virginity was later elaborated by Vossius in 1668. According to him, if jet is given in water to a female, it will have an immediate diuretic effect if she is not a virgin but none if she is. Vossius thinks that this is most useful if: 'the more wanton women are convinced that by the secret power of stones their secret vices can be brought to public notice.'

Another Roman writer, Solinus, in the 3rd century AD, mentions Britain as the source of jet. In 1587 Golding quotes him as saying:

> 'Moreover, to the intent to passe the larger abundance of sundry mettals (whereof Britaine hath many rich venes on all sides). Here is a store of the stone called Geate, and ye best kind of it. If ye domand ye beautie of it, it is a black jewell: if the qualitie, it is of no weight; if the nature, it burneth in water, and goeth out in Oyle; if the power, rubbe it till it be warme, and it holdeth such things as are laide to it as Amber doth.'

The fallacy about the oil and water is still being perpetuated here, but Solinus does distinguish between jet and amber unlike many of his contemporaries. Vossius in 1668 begins his account with the words, 'A type of amber too is jet'.

It is quite probable that some of the jet which the Romans obtained from Turkey was not of a very good quality. They were undoubtedly impressed by the excellent jet found in Britain and during the 3rd and 4th centuries AD they made extensive use of it. It was particularly popular for amulets and good luck tokens. The magical property associated with it in the Bronze Age was probably passed down through the Celts to the Romans.

A typical Roman pendant made of jet which was found in Vindolanda, a fort on Hadrian's wall, has on one side a profile of a male and a female, while on the reverse are clasped hands (Birley, 1970). Many pendants of this type have been found on Roman sites both in Britain and on the continent. Another popular design on pendants was the Medusa head. Four of these have been found in York and more of the same design in Cologne (see Chapter 6). A fine example was found in Chelmsford. The pendants were often found with beads and have a hollow lug on the top for stringing on a necklace or a thong (*Figure 3.3*).

Figure 3.3 A Roman jet betrothal medallion found in York. About 4th century AD. Size 40 × 49 mm

York, which was founded in AD 71, was a major Roman town (known as Eburacum) and many jet artifacts have been found there and in the surrounding area (RCHM, 1962). More important, a Roman jet workshop was discovered under the old railway station. Here rough jet and half worked pieces were unearthed. One piece showed signs of having been worked on a lathe. Unfortunately no tools were found, but it is likely that the Roman workmen would take their tools with them when they left.

By the 3rd century AD York was an important political, military and trade centre and a road connected it over the moors to the east coast. It is likely that York was the focus of the jet industry at that time and from there jet ornaments were sent to all parts of the Roman Empire (see Chapter 6).

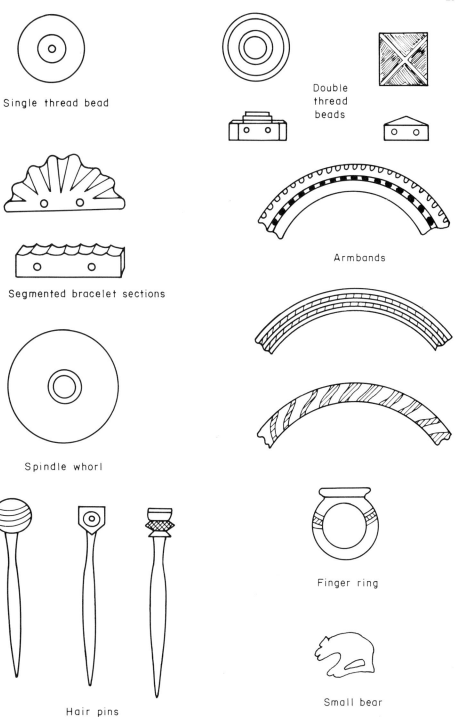

Single thread bead

Double thread beads

Segmented bracelet sections

Armbands

Spindle whorl

Hair pins

Finger ring

Small bear

Figure 3.4 Examples of Romano-British jet artefacts

The Romans made necklaces, pendants, bracelets, rings and hairpins as well as knife and mirror handles, spindle whorls and distaves. They also produced small figures of animals and statuettes of divinities and inlay for furniture. (See *Figure 3.4.*) Finds of these articles have been reported from York, Colchester, Silchester, Cirencester, Leicester, Lincoln, Malton, Goldsborough and from many other places including sites in Wales.

The Roman bracelets were of two types, either a solid armlet, made in one piece, or a segmented bracelet made of many thin segments strung side by side. The armlets were usually circular but occasionally polygonal. Sometimes they were plain and without decoration, at others with grooves, fluting or notches around the edge. The segmented bracelets consisted of many parts which were usually semi-circular and graduated. Each piece was tapered so that the inside was narrower than the outside. Each section had two perforations for threading (*Figure 3.5*).

Figure 3.5 A Victorian bracelet made in the Roman style consisting of fluted, semi-circular pieces

Beads were also sometimes double threaded, but the smaller ones had only one perforation. A small ring shaped disc was a common form of bead. Sometimes it was simply decorated. Three small jet bears have been found, one each in York, Malton and Colchester. They may have been children's toys, but since they were drilled from front to rear, it is more likely that they were worn as pendants or as the central figure in a necklace. Two similar bears have been found in Germany.

It is probable that the jet was worked in much the same way as it had been since the Bronze Age except that lathes were in use from the 1st century AD onwards. The jet could have been polished with paraffin, lampblack and linseed oil which were all available to the Romans.

In a survey of art in Britain under the Romans, Toynbee (1964) says that all the finds 'share a markedly stylized manner of treatment and a certain crudity of execution which are strongly suggestive of native workmanship'. This rather unflattering statement supports the view that the jet objects found in Britain and the German Rhineland were all made in Britain and by native craftsmen, rather than by Roman artists working either in Germany or in Britain.

Roman glass of the type made in the Rhineland has been found in York and as there were good sea communications between eastern England and the Rhineland there is a possibility that jet was traded for glass.

After the Roman armies left in the 4th century AD Britain entered the Dark Ages. For the next 500 years she was continually under attack from invading armies. Little remains of the jewellery of this period. The magnificent Sutton Hoo burial is one of the few examples of the art of the Saxon goldsmiths.

The use of jet continued in a small way, for there are references to it in the literature. The Venerable Bede (673–735 AD) in his *History of the English Church and People* refers to jet in the very first chapter:

'The land has rich veins of many metals including copper, iron, lead and silver. There is also much black jet of fine quality which sparkles in firelight: when burned it drives away snakes, and, like amber, when it is warmed by friction it clings to whatever is applied to it.'

The Saxon Monastery in Whitby, known then as Streanaeshalch, was built in the 7th century (see Chapter 4). When the ruins of this abbey were excavated in the 19th century, a few pieces of jet were found. Later literature refers to rings and crosses of jet worn by the monks (Chapter 4).

This abbey was one of many sacked by the Vikings, but later the invaders settled down to a pastoral life, renamed the town Vitby (white town) and no doubt rediscovered the beauty of jet.

The Vikings

In the 9th century the town of Eburacum, which had had a considerable jet trade under the Romans, became the Viking city of Jorvik (from which the modern name York is derived). From 867 to 1068 it was one of the most important trading centres in western Europe. Recent excavations have brought to light many objects of jet, such as the cross shown in *Figure 3.6*. This cross, found in York, and a similar one found in Pontefract are both of the same design and are decorated with yellow circles of orpiment. Orpiment was a widely used pigment known at the time as

Figure 3.6 A replica of the jet cross found in the Coppergate excavations in York. Size 20 × 38 mm

King's yellow. It was a natural substance, arsenic trisulphide, and was highly poisonous.

It was not only in Yorkshire that the Vikings made use of jet. Studies of Viking graves from the north of Scotland to Scandinavia have shown numerous examples of jet jewellery and small carvings. These have included rings and beads and many small figures of animals. Snakes were common and were probably used as amulets. Jet jewellery was found in the graves of both men and women situated in the Orkneys, Shetland and Faroes and in the north-east of Scotland. In Scandinavia jet jewellery was also found on the south-west coast of Norway, in Sweden, Finland and Denmark. Two jet pendants have been discovered in Norway. One shaped like a snake is similar in appearance to a coiled snake pendant from York. The other consists of two bears gripping each other head to toe, forming a ring. The fore legs of one animal hold the hind legs of the other which grips its neck (*Figure 3.7*). Similar pendants have been found carved in amber (Shetelig, 1944; Peterson, 1959).

Figure 3.7 Left: A jet snake from Longva, Haram, Norway. Diameter 42 mm. *Right*: The gripping bears pendant from Tresfjord Norway. Diameter 45 mm

No work has been done to establish the origin of the Viking jet. Small deposits did occur in Scotland, but it is probable that the reputation of Yorkshire jet had lasted since Roman times.

Jet was used for making dice and chessmen as well as jewellery. A jet dice found in Lincoln (Mann, 1982) is probably Roman, but a chessman found in York (MacGregor, 1982) is considered to be of Norse workmanship. Its two faces bear six ring and dot incisions and there are similar marks on the head, five on one side and three on the other. A similar jet chessman was found in Grimes Graves, Norfolk (now in Norwich Castle Museum) but it has not been dated. The British Museum has a jet playing piece found in Bawdsey, Suffolk.

The medieval period

In the years between the Viking era and the 19th century, jet appears to have been used mainly for ecclesiastical jewellery. Crosses, rosaries and rings were made and there are records showing that these were ordered by the monks of Whitby Abbey. In the abbey account rolls for the year 1394 is the entry 'Item for VII rings of gagate to Robert Car VIId', and in 1436 William Salvayne, armiger to the Abbot of Whitby, in his will bequeathed to his brother John, 'a large pair of jet rosary beads' and to his sister Sybil a ' rosary of coral and jet gauds' (Young, 1817).

In Whitby museum is a cross, dating from the 14th century, which was found attached to a witching post in a cottage in Egton in Yorkshire, and in Scarborough museum there is a jet cross of Anglian workmanship (*Figure 3.8*) (Rowntree, 1931).

It is said that, in the 17th century, jet rosaries and crucifixes were taken from Whitby to York by a certain Christopher Stonas, or Stonehouse, to be used by the Catholics who had been imprisoned in York Castle for their religious beliefs.

Figure 3.8 A jet cross of Anglian workmanship found on a skeleton of the 10th century in Scarborough

The magical properties of jet were still appreciated in the Middle Ages and when allied to the symbolism of the cross provided a very potent protection against all forms of evil. It was also widely believed that jet was a protection against dogs and so was worn by poachers.

In 1598 there is a reference to John Carlill, a jet worker who had a house near the bridge in Whitby, and in 1614 the North Riding Sessions Roll contains entries of 'jeaters' from Skinningrove.

Marbode, The Bishop of Rennes from 1067–1081, wrote a lapidary in which he describes jet in great detail. No doubt most of his information is taken from earlier Roman writers and somewhat embellished.

'Lycia her jet in medicine commends;
But chiefest, that which distant Britain sends,

Black light and polished, to itself it draws
If warmed by friction near adjacent straws.
Though quenched by oil, its smouldering embers raise
Sprinkled by water, a still fiercer blaze;
It cures the dropsy, shakey teeth are fixed,
Washed with the powder'd stone in water mixed.
The female womb its piercing fumes relieve,
Nor epilepsy can this test deceive;
From its deep hole it lures the viper fell,
And chases away the powers of hell;
It heals the swelling plagues that gnaw the heart,
And baffles spells and magic's noxious art.
This by the wise and surest test is styled
Of virgin purity by lust defiled.
Three days in water steeped, the draught bestows
Ease to the pregnant womb in travail's throes.' (King, 1860)

In 1613 Michael Drayton wrote a poem, *Polyolbion*, in which these lines appear:

'Let me but see the man
That in one tract can show the wonders that I can,
Like Whitby's self I think, there's none can show but I,
O'er whose attractive earth there may us wild geese flye.
The rocks at Moultgrave too my glories forth to set,
Out of their crannied cleeves can give you perfect jet.'   (Drayton, 1613)

References

The Bronze Age

BATEMAN, T., *Vestiges of the antiquities of Derbyshire*, John Russell Smith, London (1846)

BESWICK, P., 'Report on the shale industry at Swine Sty', *Transactions of the Hunter Archaeological Society*, **10**, III (1975)

CRAW, J. H. 'On a jet necklace from a cist at Poltalloch, Argyle', *Proceedings of the Society of Antiquities of Scotland*, **63**, (1928)

COUTTS, H., *Tayside before history*, Dundee Museum and Art Gallery Publication (1971)

ELGEE, F., *Early man in North East Yorkshire*, printed for the author by John Bellows, Gloucester (1930)

EVANS, SIR J., *The ancient stone implements of Great Britain*, Longmans, Green and Co., London (1897)

HAWKES, J., *Guide to the prehistoric and Roman monuments in England and Wales*, Chatto and Windus, London (1976)

MORRISON, A., 'A Bronze Age burial site near South Mound, Houston, Renfrewshire', *Glasgow Archaeological Journal*, **6**, (1979)

MORTIMER, J. R., *Forty years researches in British and Saxon burial mounds of East Yorkshire*, Brown, London (1905)

RAISTRICK, A., *Prehistoric Yorkshire*, Dalesman Publishing Co., Clapham via Lancaster (1976)

THOMS, L. M., *Some short cist burials from Tayside*, Dundee Museums and Art Gallery Publication (1980)

The Roman period

BEDE, THE VENERABLE, *A History of the English Church and People*, Penguin Edn., 1956

BIRLEY, R., 'Vindolanda', *Current Archaeology*, **2**, 12 (1970)

DRURY, P. J., 'Romano-British jet objects from Chelmsford', *Journal of the Society of Antiquities*, Oxford University Press, London (1973)

GOLDING, A., *The excellent and pleasant works of Julius Solinus Polyhistor*, Thomas Hacket (1587)

HENIG, M., 'A corpus of Roman engraved gemstones from the British Isles', *British Archaeological Reports,* **8,** parts 1 and 2, Oxford (1974)

LAWSON, A. J., 'Shale and jet objects from Silchester', *Archaeologia* (1976)

MACGREGOR, A., 'Roman finds from Skeldergate and Bishophill', *The Archaeology of York,* **17/2** (1978)

MANN, J. E. 'Early Medieval finds from Flaxengate'. *The Archaeology of Lincoln,* **XIV/ I** (1982)

PLINY, THE ELDER, *Natural History,* Vol. 6 BOSTOCK, J. and RILEY, H. T. (eds.) Bohn, London, (1857)

SOLINUS, *Collectanea Rerum Memorabilium,* **22,** 11 (3rd century) *see* Goldring (1587)

TOYNBEE, J. M. C. *Art in Britain under the Romans* Oxford, Clarendon Press (1964)

VOSSIUS, G. J. *De Theologia Gentilii* Blaev. Amsterdam, Lib. VI (1668)

RCHM, *An inventory of the Historical Monuments in the City of York: Vol 1 Eburacum, Roman York,* Royal Commission of Historical Monuments (1962)

The Viking era

GRAHAM-CAMPBELL, J., *Viking Artefacts,* British Museum Publication (1980)

MACGREGOR, A., 'Industry and commerce in Anglo-Scandinavian York', *in, Viking age York and the North,* HALL, R. A. (ed.) CBA research report 27 (1978)

MACGREGOR, A., 'Anglo-Scandinavian finds from Lloyds Bank pavement and other sites', *in, The Archaeology of York,* CBA report 17/3 (1982)

MANN, J. E., 'Early Medieval finds from Flaxengate', *in, The Archaeology of Lincoln,* **XIV/1,** CBA research report (1982)

PETERSON, J., *Rogaland i vikingtiden,* **11,** Stavanger Museums Arbok (1959)

SHETELIG, H., *Smykker av jet i norske vikingefunn,* Bergens Museums Arbok (1944)

WATERMAN, D. M. 'Late Saxon, Viking and early Medieval finds from York', *Archaeologia,* **97,** (1959)

The Middle Ages

DRAYTON, M., *Polyolbion,* Lownes, Browne Helme and Busbie (1613)

KING, C. W., *Antique Gems,* London (1860)

PEERS, C., RALEGH RADFORD, C. A., 'The Saxon Monastery of Whitby', *Archaeologia,* **89,** (1943)

ROWNTREE, A. (ed.), *The History of Scarborough.* J. M. Dent and Sons, London (1931)

YOUNG, G. *A history of Whitby,* Vol. 2, Clarke and Medd (1817)

Chapter 4

The Whitby jet industry

They told how in their convent-cell
A Saxon princess once did dwell
The lovely Edelfled:
And how, of thousand snakes, each one
Was changed into a coil of stone
When Holy Hilda prayed

Scott

A brief history of Whitby

Whitby is a small picturesque seaside resort on the north-east coast of England. It lies at the mouth of the river Esk, which divides the oldest part of the town on the east side from the newer west side. A good description of Whitby may be had from a most unlikely source, the book *Dracula* by Bram Stoker (1927).

The town is dominated by the ruins of St. Hilda's Abbey (*Figure 4.1*) which stands on the top of a cliff and is approached by a flight of 199 stone steps. These were built in the year 1370. Previously access to the abbey was by a steep path, now known as the donkey road, which runs alongside the steps.

At the bottom of the steps, on the right, leading to the sea, is Henrietta Street, whose small houses were built in the 18th century. Here many jet workers lived in the 19th century, some working in rooms or garretts, others in small wooden huts built precariously into the side of the cliff and held up by wooden props. In 1787 and again in 1870 landslides swept away many of the huts and houses.

In the opposite direction at the bottom of the steps lies Church Street, the oldest street in the town. There were many shops selling jet in Church Street in the 19th century, and some are still there today. Opening off these streets are small narrow alleyways, known locally as yards, some with intriguing names such as Cockpit Yard, Elbow Yard and Arguments Yard. The last is named after a family of that name and does not, as might be supposed, refer to their quarrelsome nature. A visit to any of these yards in the last century would bring the sound of turning lathes and clouds of jet dust would surround the unwary visitor who ventured to enter the small rooms where the jet was being worked (Linskill, 1885).

The larger jet manufacturers had their premises on the west side of the river in what are now the main streets of the town, Flowergate, Haggersgate and Baxtergate. Gate is a Viking word meaning a road or a way. Yet here too, at the height of the industry, all the small side yards were filled with jet workrooms.

Wherever one stands in Whitby today there is a view of the Abbey ruins and it is not surprising that so many articles of jet were decorated with an engraving of the Abbey of St. Hilda (*Figure 4.2*). Its history goes back to the 7th century. At that time King Oswy of Northumbria (*Figure 4.3*) was at war with the heathen King

Figure 4.1 The ruins of St. Hilda's Abbey, Whitby

Figure 4.2 An engraving of Whitby Abbey was used to decorate many of the items of jewellery or ornaments such as this brooch made in the 19th century

Figure 4.3 A carved jet plaque supposed to represent King Oswy of Northumberland and his wife

Penda of Mercia. Oswy promised that if he should defeat Penda he would provide 'twelve gifts of land for the founding of monasteries and would give his one year old daughter Elfled (or Æfleda) to the religious life'. In 655, although vastly outnumbered, he did defeat Penda and made good his promise, so that in 657 the monastery at Whitby was founded with Hilda (later St. Hilda) as its Abbess. At the time it was called Streanaeshalch Abbey. Sometimes spelt Streoneshalh (there is a variety of spellings) the word meant 'The Bay of the Watchtower'. In view of its commanding position, it is quite possible that there was a watchtower on the site in Roman times.

Elfled duly entered the monastery and after the death of Hilda in 680 became Abbess for the next 33 years. She, her father and mother are buried in the Abbey. In 664 Whitby Abbey was the site of the famous Synod of Whitby which fixed the date of Easter, thus reconciling the Roman and Celtic Churches.

The arms of Whitby Abbey have three gold snakes on a blue field surmounted by a crosier and mitre. The snakes commemorate the legend of St. Hilda who drove out all the snakes from the area and turned them into stones. These are the ammonites which are found in large numbers in the cliffs around Whitby. The local people call them snake stones, and in earlier times commented on the fact that they never seemed to have any heads. Thus the crest of the town bears three ammonites without the snakes' heads.

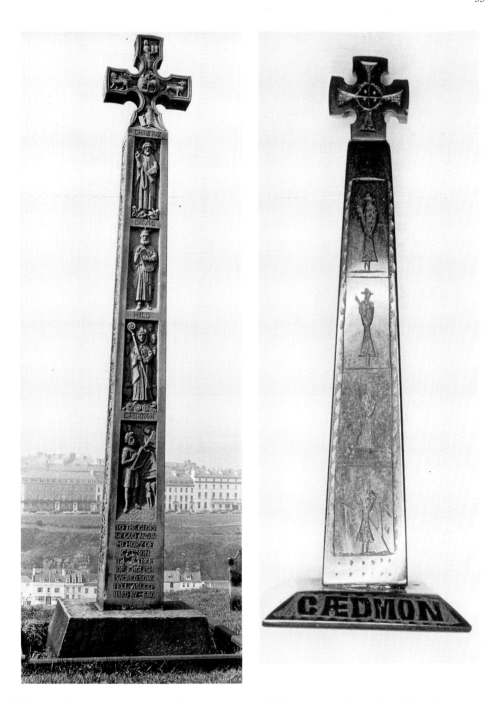

Figure 4.4 Left: Caedmon's cross which was erected in 1898 in memory of 'the father of English poetry'.
Right: A replica of the cross made in jet, many of which were sold as tourist souvenirs. Height 88 mm

The original abbey, which was probably a building of wood and thatch, was sacked by the Vikings in 867. The present ruins are of a building started in 1140. At one time the abbey boasted a tower over 30 m high, but this fell down suddenly in 1830.

In front of the abbey today stands a stone cross. This was erected in 1898 in memory of the Saxon poet Caedmon (*Figure 4.4*). Caedmon was a servant in the abbey who late in life had a vision wherein he was told to sing of all the principal events in sacred history. He is sometimes called the father of English poetry and many small copies of the cross were later made in jet.

In 1540 Whitby had 200 inhabitants. In the 17th century alum working was introduced into the area and the population increased to 3000. In the 18th century Whitby became a well-known shipbuilding port, and is nowadays associated with the names of such famous seafarers as the Scoresby family. William Scoresby was the inventor of the 'Crow's nest' look-out used on old whaling ships, and he also achieved the highest latitude approaching the North Pole in a sailing ship in 1806.

Probably the best known seafarer whose statue now looks out to sea from the top of the West Cliff is Captain James Cook. He was not born in Whitby, but in the small village of Marton, in 1728, the son of a farm worker and one of nine children. He was apprenticed to John Walker, a master mariner of Whitby, and from here he sailed on his famous voyages of discovery. All his ships, the *Endeavor, Resolution, Adventure* and *Discovery*, were built at Whitby. In 1768 he sailed on his first voyage on the *Endeavor*. He was killed in the Sandwich Islands in 1779 at the age of 51. In the 19th century this local hero was the favourite subject for cameos carved by the jet workers (*Figure 4.5*).

Thus, in the 18th century, shipbuilding and whaling were the prime industries of Whitby. At that time jet carving was still more of a hobby than an industry. Local people finding jet on the beaches would amuse themselves by making crude beads or crosses. The seamen who went on the whaling ships, often for voyages of two or three years, would take some jet from home to carve in their spare time in much the same manner as some cut scrimshaw.

Yet as the 19th century progressed and steam ships gradually took over from sail, so too the jet industry gradually came to be of more importance in the town than shipbuilding.

Start of the industry

The change started at the turn of the 19th century, and local history attributes it to the arrival in the town of a retired naval officer. The following account was originally written in 1854 and has been rewritten so many times since, each time with a few more spelling mistakes, that it seems best to quote it here in the original form in which it appeared in the *Whitby Treasury* of 1854 as reported by Woodwark (1922).

'About the year 1800 however, a painter named Robert Jefferson who is still living and one John Carter, who kept a public house in Haggersgate, a native of

Figure 4.5 Top: A pair of earrings carved by E. H. Greenbury. The one on the left bears a cameo of Captain Cook. The identity of the gentleman on the right is not known. Size of earrings 26 × 57 mm. *Bottom*: E. H. Greenbury's trade card

Bedale, and who is often spoken of by the name of Katterfelto, in consequence of having married the widow of Gustavus Katterfelto (a Prussian who delivered lectures on science in the town hall Whitby) began to make beads and crosses of jet with files and knives. A necklace made in this barbarous manner was sold for £1.1s. A short time afterwards, Captain Tremlett, a naval pensioner came to reside at Whitby, who, stepping into Carter's house, observed Jefferson and Carter pursuing the art in its rude state. He showed them some amber beads which he had turned on a lathe, and said he would ask some turner if jet could not be turned in the same way. The trio went to one Matthew Hill, who had the workshop lately occupied by Mr Thomas Horsman. Hill succeeded in making beads but had no confidence that the art could be pursued to profit. Tremlett, however, agreed to pay him his wages as a turner if he would work for him in the making of jet ornaments.'

Thus it seems that the first jet workshop was set up at Carter's house in Haggersgate in about 1808. In a few years there were as many as 10 shops making crosses, beads and snuff boxes.

At this time Whitby was isolated by the bleak North Yorkshire Moors, the crossing of which, particularly in winter, was regarded as highly dangerous. At the time it was usual for people to journey to London by sea, but this journey too was hazardous and passengers were advised to make a will before sailing – a suggestion which was unlikely to reassure those of a nervous disposition. It was only in 1759 that a coach road from Pickering was built over the moors to Whitby. The first railway was constructed in 1836. Built by George Stephenson at a cost of £120 000 it was 24 miles long and powered by a single horse. Steam trains finally came on the scene in 1845.

Thus in the early days of the jet industry the marketing of the product was beset by difficulties of distribution, and the railways were probably the first factor to encourage the growth of this new industry.

The Victorian invention of the annual holiday, and the easier access provided by the railways, encouraged the growth of Whitby as a popular seaside resort where the new fashion for 'sea bathing' could be safely experienced.

The Victorians had a love of souvenirs and felt obliged to take home from their holidays examples of local products, either for themselves or as gifts for their family and friends. Thus an item of jet from Whitby became obligatory and all helped to further the growth of the industry. This did give rise to some jealousy from neighbouring resorts. In 1873 the *Scarborough Gazette* wrote:

'Surely no modern manufacture of trumpery ever rivalled this in ugliness. With a refinement of cruelty some workers embed sections of ammonites in it; others, and this is the ne plus ultra of richness, surround it with a fretwork of alabaster; and you may have a card tray of this glittering inconclusive material with the classic features of Victor Emmanuel staring at you in jet from the bottom. One wonders who can buy such things but there are some people who must have the speciality of the place they are in, however base and trivial it may be.' (Bower, 1873)

This did not worry the Whitbians in the least, since they watched their industry flourish.

Famous manufacturers

By 1850, there were 12 manufacturers and many individuals engaged in the craft. Many well-known names appeared on the scene, such as the Bingant family. A French emigré of that name settled in Whitby during the French revolution, and his son opened one of the first shops to sell jet in Church Street in 1820. The family name was associated with the industry for many generations.

In the early days, one of the biggest manufacturers and progenitor of a long line of successful craftsmen was Isaac Greenbury. In 1851 he exhibited jet necklaces, brooches and other ornaments at the Great Exhibition in London. The official catalogue shows his name under the title of 'works in precious metals etc.'. As a result of the Great Exhibition, jet jewellery became known on the continents of Europe and America and Mr Isaac Greenbury was honoured by an order for a set of bracelets for the Empress of France. Twenty-two years later, in 1873, his nephew, Edward Heselton Greenbury, was one of the most talented sculptors of jet to belong to the industry. When the Worshipful Company of Turners of London offered prizes for the best article of stone turning, he won the silver medal, the Freedom of the Company and the Freedom of the City of London. E. H. Greenbury was renowned for his cameos and busts of famous people, and some of his work can be seen in Whitby museum. In the Rotunda museum in Scarborough there are sculptures with which he won prizes in America. The Greenbury family was outstanding among the more talented craftsmen at the height of the industry, about 1870–80 (*Figures 4.5* and *4.6*).

Another prominent manufacturer of the mid-century was Thomas Andrew, who, in 1850, was already advertising himself as 'Jet Ornament Manufacturer to Her

Figure 4.6 A cameo of a man's head by E. H. Greenbury. Size 47 × 54 mm (shown here approximately actual size)

Figure 4.7 Mrs Gladstone wearing jet beads, locket and bracelet after her visit to Whitby in 1872

Figure 4.8 The cameo head of the Empress Eugenie on a jet plaque made by Charles Bryan for the Paris Exhibition of 1876. Size 107 × 135 mm

Figure 4.9 The cameo head of the Emperor Napoleon III made by Charles Bryan for the Paris exhibition of 1876. Size 112 × 140 mm. This plaque and that in *Figure 4.8* won first prize

Majesty Queen Victoria'. One family who began in the early days of the industry and spanned the whole era were the Bryans. They were eventually the biggest manufacturers in Whitby. The firm was established by George Bryan in 1810, taken over first by his son George and later by his other son Charles, in 1848. By 1873 the latter had built up the business to employ 170 men. His foreman was Jasper

Figure 4.10 A parure of mourning jewellery by Charles Bryan

Bingant, a descendant of the French family mentioned above. At the height of the industry the Bryans had retail outlets all over Britain and abroad. They had shops in London, Brighton, Leeds, Liverpool, Paris and Amsterdam. In 1872 the Prime Minister and Mrs Gladstone visited the workshop and *Figure 4.7* shows Mrs Gladstone wearing jet. Charles Bryan died, aged 64, in 1897 at a time when he could witness the decline of the industry to which he had devoted his whole life (*Figures 4.8, 4.9* and *4.10*).

Trade directories of the 19th century provide records of the men who made the Whitby jet industry such a success. Some of these are given in the Appendices, but one or two other names should have particular mention because known examples of their work can be seen in Whitby museum. These are James Ainsley (*Figures 4.11* and *4.12*), William Stonehouse, Matthew Snowdon and John Speedy (*Figures, 4.13* and *4.14*). The superb cameos of the Speedy family are very characteristic in style and explain why the jet carvers seldom signed their work. Each man specialized in a particular field and it was said that each could distinguish the work of any of his colleagues at a glance. The Speedy family were well known in the trade; but it is sad to think that the last surviving member, who worked in jet and specialized in inlay work, ended his days in the workhouse.

One very well-known manufacturer was William Wright whose manufacturing shop and retail shop were on Marine Parade. In 1890, the renowned Whitby

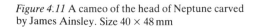

Figure 4.11 A cameo of the head of Neptune carved by James Ainsley. Size 40 × 48 mm

Figure 4.12(a) A portrait of James Ainsley

Fig. 4.12 (b): James Ainsley's advertisement in Kelly's Directory 1880

HORNES' GENERAL ADVERTISI

Printed by HORNE & SON, Whitby, SATURDAY, APF

Dark Bay
gh, will run
Mr. GREEN,

act, all that
ING MULE,
1871 by G.
stores.—For
, Black Lion

te Moyats
pply to Mr.

large con-
OUGH and
and in good
some of the
attention of

st Pier, and

on HAY,
JNO. STAIN-
PE, Lythe.
PES.
and 6 inch
S and PAN
ser Street,

me CAR-
n deceased.
Whitby.

USES in
W FIELD
ATE CON-

eckwith ;
k, occupied

folman.

LAND,
rs, Whitby.

T. H. READMAN, PAINTER & DECORATOR, CARVER & GILDER, CHURCH STREET respectfully announces that he has now on hand a large Stock of elegant PAPER-HANGINGS PANEL DECORATIONS, &c. GILDING IN ALL ITS BRANCHES by a first class Workman.
WASHABLE GILT MOULDINGS for Rooms, Picture Frames &c., &c.

PRIZE JET.   PRIZE JET.

G. & J. SPEEDY, No. 7, FLOWERGATE, and 9, CLIFF STREET, Whitby ; 5, Parliament Street, Harrogate ; and 177A, Lord Street, Southport ; *(who had the honour of receiving to their Establishment the Award of the First Prize for Brooches, and the Prize for the Best Design and Workmanship by Youths, at the Whitby Institute Exhibition*, 1863,*)* respectfully solicit the Nobility, Gentry, and Visitors to Whitby, to inspect their superb assortment of JET ORNAMENTS, which will be found of the most fashionable designs, and for workmanship not to be surpassed.

J. P. FAWCETT, TAILOR & WOOLLEN DRAPER, No. 50, FLOWERGATE, Whitby,
FROM
Thompson and Felix's, Rue Lue le Grand, Paris ; and Meyers & Mortimer's Conduit Street, London, Tailors to H.R.H. the Prince of Wales, the Royal Family, and the *élite* of Europe.
LADIES' RIDING HABITS, UNIFORMS, LIVERIES, &c.

J. WALLER, PHOTOGRAPHER, PIER PORTRAIT ROOMS. Carte de Visite Portraits, CABINET PORTRAITS, PHOTOGRAPHS, from Miniature to Life-size, Coloured in Water or Oil.
A large collection of " Carte," Stereoscopic, Cabinet, and other Views.
J. WALLER (Whitby).—We have to thank this artist | and others, not more charming for their graceful and for some *carte* portraits of various kinds and more than | easy *pose* than attractive for their faultless photo-
average excellence. Among them are groups of children | graphy.—*The British Journal of Photography.*

W. LANGDALE, having secured a First-class SCULPTOR, purposes extending his business in the department of TOMBS, MEMORIALS, HEADSTONES, CENOTAPHS, and TABLETS, in Marble, Granite, or Freestone, of the finest quality, at his New Premises, 36, BAXTERGATE, and intends to bring out designs and workmanship not to be excelled, and at very moderate charges.
Designs for approval free.   Works—36, BAXTERGATE.   Office—61, BAXTERGATE, WHITBY.

BEST WHITBY JET AND
LONDON-MADE JEWELLERY.

C HAPMAN & CO., CENTRE SHOP, FRONT OF THE CROWN HOTEL,
FLOWERGATE, WHITBY,
(Late of 2, GOLDEN LION BANK,)
Respectfully inform the Visitors to, and the Inhabitants of Whitby that they have OPENED the above Establishment with a large and choich Stock of
JET ORNAMENTS,
principally made under the supervision of one of the Firm.
The Stock of JEWELLERY consists of Suits, Brooches, Earrings, Lockets Rings, Pins, Necklets, Studs, &c.,
in great variety, suitable for BIRTHDAY and WEDDING PRESENTS, &c.

Figure 4.13 The front page of the *Whitby Gazette* for 25th April 1874 showing an advertisement for the Speedy family

Figure 4.14 A cameo head by J. Speedy which shows his characteristic style. Size 55 × 61 mm (shown approximately actual size)

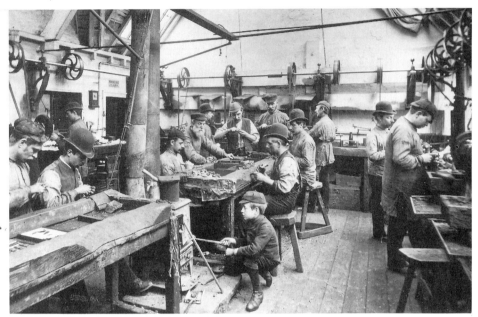

Figure 4.15(a) William Wright's workshop photographed by F. M. Sutcliffe in 1890. The gentleman seated second from the left is Mr J. W. Barker who can be seen in later years in *Figures 4.26* and *4.29*. He was the last man to be indentured into the jet trade. The names of the men are from left to right, G. L. Wilson, J. W. Barker, R. Headlam, John Spencer, John Headlam (Foreman), John Young, John Lyth, George Robinson, David Young, John Breakon, James Leck, William Sutherland and Arthur Gale. Master George Arthur Headlam, the Foreman's grandson, is tending the cast-iron stove on which the pot of ockamatutt is heating. The workshop is unusual in that the lathes are turned by gas engines. Notice the typical three-legged stools and the round hats worn by six of the men which were called 'Mullers'

Figure 4.15(b) William Wright's trade card

photographer F. M. Sutcliffe took a photograph of the Wright jet shop (*Figure 4.15*) and the names of all the men working in it are on record. The second from the left is J. W. Barker who was the last man to be indentured into the trade. Wright's shop was unusual in that the lathes were powered by gas engines.

The expansion of the holiday resorts is only one of the factors in the success story of the Whitby jet industry. As with all jewellery, fashion played a large part, but with jet in a unique way. It was its close association with mourning jewellery that ensured jet's success and at the same time sowed the seeds of its demise.

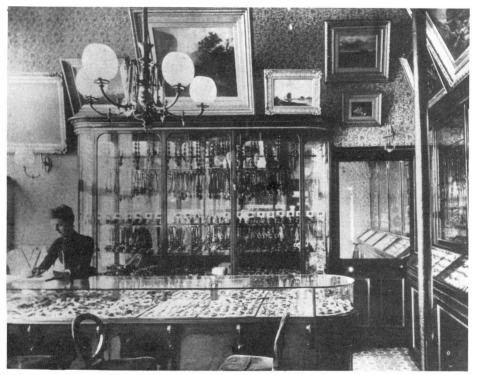

Figure 4.16 William Wright's retail shop on Marine Parade in 1890; the mirrored door on the right led into the workshop. The glass counter, empty now, can still be seen in Whitby museum

The association of jet with mourning

Throughout history there have been certain rituals connected with mourning. Each society has had its own customs, but probably none was as strict and as complicated as that of Victorian England (Taylor, 1983). Victorian women were very socially minded, very concious of class, and appear to have always been striving to attain the class above the one in which they started life. Because of this they had a strictly laid down pattern of behaviour and it was a social disaster to deviate even slightly from it. Furthermore it was essential to dress exactly according to the prevailing fashion and the arbiter of fashion was the court and ultimately the Queen.

Thus when a member of the Royal family died, the court went into mourning and so did those ladies of fashion who wished to appear associated with the aristocracy. When George IV died on June 26th 1830, the Lord Chamberlain's office issued a decree describing the exact type of mourning clothing to be worn and ending with the unequivocal statement 'the ornaments will be jet'. Queen Victoria was meticulous in observing the correct period of mourning, not only for her own family but for other heads of state or for people of importance. When the Duke of Wellington died in 1852 not only the court, but the whole country wore mourning

Figure 4.17(a) A young woman in mourning dress *circa* 1870. Note the large quantity of crepe used in the dress. She is wearing a matching set of earrings, brooch, necklace and watch chain

for him. In 1861, on the death of Prince Albert, the Queen, then only 42 years old, plunged the court into deepest mourning which she herself maintained until her death at the age of 82.

The required periods of mourning for various relatives were rigidly decreed by etiquette. A widow mourned her husband for 2½ years. During the first year she was virtually a social outcast, rarely leaving the house. She wore black, entirely covered by crepe, and no ornaments other than black jewellery. According to the strictest rules this should not even be shiny, but should have a dull matt surface. It would appear that jet, with its high polish, should not have been worn during the first year. Nevertheless it seems that only the greatest stickler adhered to this

Figure 4.17(b) A lady in her second year of widowhood wearing crepe on her bodice and sleeves and jet beads on her skirt. She wears jet earrings, a three-strand faceted necklace, a very large brooch and a bracelet (probably a pair) decorated with cameos, *circa* 1870

tradition because photographs of the time show much jet being worn even in the first stage of mourning (*Figure 4.17a*).

In the second year of mourning (*Figure 4.17b*) a widow was still in black but with less crepe and with more decoration allowed on the dress. Now as much jet as she liked could be worn, and lavish use was made of French jet (black glass) trimmings on capes and gowns. In the final six months of her mourning, a widow could wear clothes of any material provided it was black. Occasionally a little relaxation was allowed into grey or mauve, but black jewellery was still worn together perhaps with pearls and diamonds.

In contrast to this long period of mourning by widows, a widower was only obliged to mourn his wife for three months. If during that time he remarried, and this he was encouraged to do, his new wife went into mourning for her predecessor. The decreed periods of mourning for other relatives decreased as the relationship became less close. Thus it was one year for a child, six months for a brother or sister, three months to six weeks for cousins and so on. In fact, many women, after the loss of a beloved child, adopted black for the rest of their lives. Even in the early 20th century this was not uncommon. The author's own grandmother did so, and probably many readers will recall their grandparents wearing black.

Victorian fashion

With the large families common in Victorian times, and the high infant mortality, it is not surprising that many women, once married, would find themselves in mourning for the greater part of their lives. All this, of course, generated a demand for jet jewellery, and from 1861 the industry was hardly able to meet the demand for its product. The jet workers were thriving and, while making more money than they had ever done, they little thought that this association with mourning would eventually contribute to the downfall of their industry.

The peak years lasted from 1851, the year of the Great Exhibition, to 1874. The value of the trade was given as £45 000 in 1860 rising to £100 000 in 1873 and in that year the manufacturing shops numbered 200, employing about 1500 men (Bower, 1873). Contemporary photographs of ladies of the 1870s and 1880s frequently show at least one jet ornament and often very much more. In 1867 the great singer, Adelina Patti, had herself photographed wearing a selection of jet jewellery and, as with the pop stars of today, the ladies followed her fashion, whether in mourning or not (*Figure 4.18*).

The clothes of the mid-19th century were particularly voluminous, culminating in the unwieldy crinoline. Small jewellery appeared insignificant with such styles and jet's light weight lent itself admirably to the design of very large and bulky jewellery. Brooches of up to 150 mm in length, beads the size of table tennis balls and very long earrings could be worn without discomfort. Jewellery of that size in metal would have pulled down the fabric of the dress, not to mention the earlobes, so large items of jet were common at this period and were light and comfortable to wear. Not only was each piece of jewellery large in size but a great deal was worn at one time. Contemporary photographs commonly show a lady wearing earrings, a

Figure 4.18 Four sisters who are wearing necklaces, brooches, pendants, earrings and bracelets of jet. It is interesting to note the decreasing size of beads from the eldest in the centre to the youngest standing behind. There was obviously a clear cut 'pecking order' in the family

Figure 4.19 A lady wearing a crinoline with jet earrings, a long jet chain, a brooch and a pair of bracelets, *circa* 1860

large brooch, a necklace and a pair of bracelets without appearing vulgar or overdone (*Figure 4.19*).

Towards the end of the century when fashions changed, clothes became more streamlined and consequently jewellery was smaller. This was bad news for the Whitby jet workers, and was just one of the reasons why their sales dropped. But in the halcyon years of the mid-century there was no thought of this, and Whitby boomed. Apart from the large manufacturing premises, there were also many individual workers who would buy a small quantity of jet from the rough jet merchant, work it at home and then sell it for the best price possible. Thus there was little organization or co-ordination in the industry. There were no guilds or unions as there were in Germany or Spain (see Chapter 6) and no central body to control jet quality or price. The picture is of everyone working to capacity, in large shop or small garret room, to fashion the product that was selling so well. The quality of the jet used and that of the finished product varied enormously, as can be seen from those articles that can still be found today.

To add to this, the supply of top quality hard jet was fast running out. To meet demand the manufacturers turned to the local soft jet and also began importing jet from France and Spain. So desperate were they for supplies that they became less and less particular about quality, and it was not always easy to distinguish soft from hard jet in the rough. As a result many expensive items began to crack soon after they were sold and gave rise to dissatisfaction among customers. When the decline in the trade in the late 1880s became obvious, attempts were made belatedly to rectify this lack of control by the introduction of a trade mark.

Training of craftsmen

In the mid-century years there could have been no thought that the trade would ever cease to prosper. Demand exceeded the supply of jet. Since all the articles were hand-made by trained craftsmen there was no way of increasing output other than by training new men. This was, however, a slow business, for a fully trained craftsman had to undergo a period of seven years apprenticeship, while those who were only qualified to turn beads still had to serve five years. Boys were often indentured into the trade at the age of 10 years (*Figure 4.20*). The last person to be indentured was J. W. Barker and his indenture can be seen in Whitby museum. Later in the 1920s he took, as his apprentice, Joseph Gourly Lyth. He was the last man to be apprenticed into the trade and one might say he was the last of the true Victorian jet workers. He entered the trade at the age of 15 and learnt the art of carving, inlaying and engraving from Mr Barker (*Figure 4.26*). Joe Lyth died in 1958 at the age of 50, but his jet shop has been preserved in the Castle museum in York.

In 1873 apprentice boys were paid about 10 shillings (50p) a week. The lesser-trained men earned from 16 shillings to £1.1s. (80p–£1.05) a week but the best workers could earn from £4 to £6 a week, which was an excellent wage for the time. Conditions of work were also quite good. The men started work in the

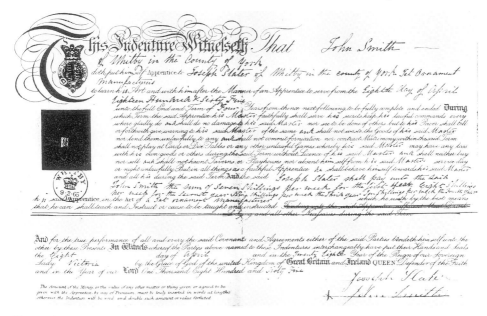

Figure 4.20 A copy of an indenture of 1874

morning as the Town Hall clock struck six, had one hour off for lunch and finished work when the clock struck six in the evening. They worked only four days a week, from Monday to Thursday. On Sundays they went to church, but it is said that Friday and Saturday were spent in the Jet Men's Arms, since all the dust made jet working a very thirsty occupation. Not an unhealthy one though, for the dust did not apparently cause any respiratory problems comparable to silicosis. Women were employed to do unskilled work, but there is no record of what they were paid.

As the industry grew it was felt that more variety was needed in the objects made. The workers were divided into two groups. The lesser-paid fashioned what might be called 'mass produced' articles such as beads, chains or the small rings which form part of the earrings. For this repetitive work little artistic ability was needed. But the other group, the true craftsmen, were artists and sculptors. It was they who produced busts and cameos of famous people, elaborately carved trays, penholders and vases of the highest quality which may be seen in the museums today. Some of these men drew their designs on paper first while others worked directly on to the jet. Even such artists as these were eventually accused of being lacking in original ideas and so in 1856 a drawing class was established at the local night school. Two years later the 'Whitby Institute of Popular Arts, Science and Literature' was affiliated to the London Society of Arts. In 1863 the first local jet exhibition was held, with prizes up to the value of £14. Such exhibitions were then held from time to time until 1883, with prizes under such headings as 'A set of brooch, bracelet and earrings', 'Best brooch of any value', 'Best brooch of retail value 10s (50p) to 20s (£1), 'A bust of the Prince Consort' and so on. In 1863 the London Society of Arts offered £10 towards the prizes, and by 1873 the total prize money was as much as £120.

Figure 4.21 A selection of bar brooches, From the top, two name brooches, one of which is misspelt and bar brooches decorated with gold stars and seed pearls, mother of pearl inlay and an ammonite. The length of the longest brooch is 63 mm

Among the prize winners in 1874 were E. H. Greenbury, John Speedy, George Tyson and John Wray, and among the youths under eighteen were Matthew Snowdon, Joseph Falkinridge and James Speedy. Articles made by many of these men can be seen in Whitby museum. In spite of their undoubted artistic ability, many of the workmen were illiterate. For those who made the name brooches (*Figure 4.21* and *5.3*) a large board was put up in the workroom spelling out the names. The men copied them onto the jet, not always with success as when Mavis became Navis. When making sectional bracelets, the matching pieces were indicated by dots or lines. Bower (1873) writes in the *Journal of the Society of Arts*: 'I saw a workmen, one of the best hands in a large shop in Whitby, able to cut the most elaborate monograms, the most accurate portraits, the most elaborate foliage, but quite unable to sign his name.'

Because they were hand carved, jet articles were never cheap. The bust of Mary Queen of Scots (*Figure 4.22*) still has the original price under the plinth. Bought in 1873, it cost £20.10s (£20.50) which could represent a year's wages for some people. It was partly the high price of jet jewellery that made it so vulnerable to competition from cheaper imitations (see Chapter 7).

The high price of jet was undoubtedly one of the reasons for the decline of the industry at the end of the 19th century, but there were other reasons too. Already

Figure 4.22 A bust of Mary Queen of Scots; an
example of the very finest workmanship. The cost
of this article in 1873 was £20.10s. Overall height
240 mm, width at base 75 mm

in 1877 a report in the *Whitby Gazette* referred to the depressed state of the trade. In 1881 the paper pointed out that the number of men employed had decreased to 600 and that they were only earning an average of £1 a week, a big drop from the £4–6 of 10 years previously. By 1884 the number had dropped to 300 and so on until in 1921 a report states that no more than 40 men were engaged, some of whom were only part time. In that year one of the major manufacturers, Mr T. Trattles, said that he had more orders from America for beads and bracelets than he could supply, because of the shortage of good hard jet of the first quality.

The sad ending to this story was given to the present author in 1980 by an elderly lady, a descendant of one of the jet families. She said that in the end Mr Trattles became so disillusioned with the trade that took all his stock to Woolworths where he sold it for a very low price.

This lady, whose family shop can still be found at the bottom of the 199 stone steps of St. Hilda's Abbey, remembers some of the old jet workers of the last century. She talks of colourful characters such as Pete Campion who had a leather

Figure 4.23 Edward Pearson who had a jet manufacturing business in Clerkenwell, London, until 1892

leg and specialized in making snake bracelets, Alf Bowron who made very small beads, and the old man who stood at the top of the 199 steps with his portable jet shop.

When jet was at the height of its popularity, there were jet workshops in several other towns. William Wright had a shop in Brighton and in Clerkenwell, London, there were a number of shops where jet jewellery was made. One of these belonged to Edward Pearson (*Figure 4.23*) whose granddaughter took many of the photographs used in this book.

The manufacture of jet ornaments in Victorian times

The manufacturing premises were known as jet shops, and these are not to be confused with the retailing establishments. The shops varied in size from those employing one or two men, to that of Charles Bryan which could accommodate up to 170 workers. These large establishments, which had separate rooms for each of the manufacturing processes, were the exception and the most common shops were those that employed about 6 to 10 men, all working in one room. Old photographs show that there were solid wooden benches around the walls to which the wheels and lathes were fitted. Down the centre of the room were benches fitted with great beams of wood and between them a cast-iron stove for heating the room and melting the glue used in the manufacturing process. Tending the stove was usually the work of the youngest apprentice (*Figure 4.15*). The independent workers had their small workshops in a shed in the garden or in a small garrett room. *Figure 4.24* shows an accurate model of one such shop.

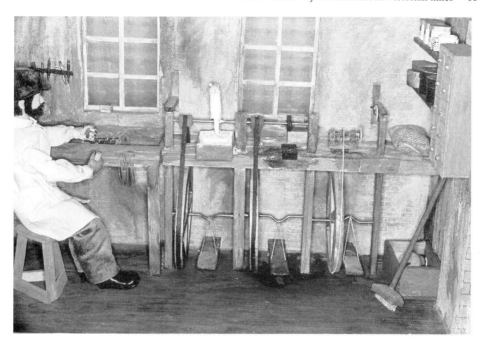

Figure 4.24 A scale model of a jet workshop. This shows the 'jettie' wearing his blue overall and ancient hat seated on a typical three-legged stool. He is chopping out with a chisel against a wooden beam on the front of his workbench. On the wall are his home-made carving tools. Suspended from the front of the bench are strips of emery paper for working the holes and hollows in the design. There are three large wooden fly wheels with two leather drive belts and one of rope turned by the foot treadles. In the first bay is a grinding wheel over a box of rotten stone; the wheel is protected by a splash cover made from an old piece of trouser leg. In the second bay is a polishing wheel and in the third a lathe fitted with a lead-cutting disc. Other discs lie in the box on the floor. On the right is a sack of rough jet and a set of drawers in which the 'jettie' kept his findings. Everything is covered with jet dust, but the floor, which would normally be littered with broken jet and other rubbish, has been newly swept for the photograph

Until recently a few old photographs were the only record of what a Victorian jet shop had looked like, but in 1977 an exciting event took place by accident. Off Flowergate, the main shopping street in Whitby, is a small cul-de-sac called Burns Yard. At the end of the dark narrow passage is a plumber's shop. One day water started to leak through the ceiling and the plumber climbed upstairs to investigate. It seems that he had never before shown any curiosity towards what existed in the upper rooms. He climbed to the landing on the first floor and then struggled up a very steep dark flight of stairs which led to a door in the attic. On opening that door he stepped back into the past, for there before him was a complete jet workshop, equipped with tools, rough jet, lapidary mountings, finished articles and with thick, thick layers of jet dust covering everything. The plumber called Whitby museum who later took out a lease on the premises, repaired the roof and windows and installed electric lighting.

This shop had belonged to one of the last three Victorian-trained craftsmen, Mr Wilfred Braithwaite, whose father and grandfather before him had been jet workers (*Figure 4.25*). Although he occupied it until the 1950s it had never been modernized and remained essentially the same as it had been in his grandfather's day. Sometime in the late 19th century, naked gas jets had been installed, but other than that the benches, the lathes and the wheels, even the old cast-iron stove which stood in the centre of the room, were still as they had been in the last century.

On each side of the room were stout wooden workbenches supported by upright posts which formed bays holding a grinding or a polishing wheel. Each lathe or wheel was turned by a leather drive belt that connected it to a large wooden fly wheel about 0.86 m in diameter which was turned by a foot treadle. The naked gas jets ran up the upright posts and were probably used for lighting. At some places along the workbench were thick beams of wood against which the jet was chopped out. Thin strips of emery paper were still attached to the bench. These were used for polishing the grooves and hollows of the design which could not be reached by the wheels.

One corner of the room was partitioned off to form a small office, perhaps for the foreman, for there was a small spy-hole cut into the wall for him to observe the men at work. Although the room was empty, it was not difficult to visualize it as it must once have been with perhaps six or more 'jetties' working there and a small boy heating the glue on the stove.

The process of manufacture

When the jet miners brought their rough jet back to Whitby, they sold it to the rough jet merchants, who included William Thompson, Thomas Hall, Elisha Walker, George Hopper and Raymond Peguero. The last-named was a Spanish jet merchant who brought jet to Whitby from Spain. On one of his frequent visits he fell in love with a Whitby girl and eventually married her and set up his business in Whitby. These men had warehouses where the jet was stored until required. They sorted the rough jet into various categories according to quality, size and thickness. Then the manufacturer would buy from the rough jet merchant exactly what he needed at any one time.

In the workshop the task of allocating the rough jet to the various workers fell to the foreman. His was a very important job. Each piece of rough jet had to be carefully studied for quality, flaws, size and thickness in order to decide what was to be made from it. Small pieces of poorer quality went for bead making. For cameos a good thick piece was required, while very thin pieces could be used for monograms. The very best quality jet had to be used for ornaments such as busts and for cigar and cigarette holders which were very difficult to drill. Some of the foremen were talented sculptors in their own right. Jasper Bingant was foreman to Charles Bryan, John Headlam to William Wright (*Figure 4.15*) and other well-known foremen were Charles Pearson, George Robinson and Jonathan Short.

As has been pointed out in Chapter 1 the rough jet when mined had a skin or spar of a bluish brown colour, from the shale in which it was found. The most highly prized jet had a blue skin from the alum shale and was found near Boulby.

First the skin was removed, using a heavy chisel of iron or steel with a handle weighted with lead (*Figure 4.25*). All the movement was done with the wrist and no

PLATE 1
A fine set of brooch and earrings comprising porcelain miniatures set in carved jet surrounds. Size of brooch, 40 × 50 mm

PLATE 2
Two pendants with porcelain miniatures set in jet and in the centre a pietra dura locket with a picture compartment on the reverse dated 1876. Size of locket, 40 × 54 mm

PLATE 3
A small jet bear decorated with turquoise made by
Zuni Indians

PLATE 4
A hand painted porcelain miniature set in jet

PLATE 5
A colourful brooch of pietra dura in a jet surround

PLATE 6
A jet bracelet set with pietra dura

PLATE 7
A jet bracelet set with a hand painted porcelain
picture of Red Riding Hood and the wolf

PLATE 8
A pair of drop earrings with hand painted porcelain
miniatures

PLATE 9
A selection of jet necklaces

Figure 4.25 Mr W. Braithwaite at his workbench showing how the spar is removed with a chisel

mallet was used. The jet was then ready for chopping out into pieces of suitable size and shape. This was done either working with the chisel, against a stout piece of wood attached to the front of the workbench, or using a disc saw fitted to the lathe. Because jet was expensive it was very important that the minimum of waste occurred at this stage. Small cut-offs could be used for beads.

The chopped out pieces were then ground on a 350 mm diameter sandstone grit wheel which took off the rough corners. The jet was wetted and held against the side of the wheel (*Figure 4.26*). It was then passed to the craftsman who would complete it by cutting, carving, engraving, inlaying or any of the specialized arts

Figure 4.26 J. W. Barker and J. G. Lyth in their workshop. Mr Barker is using the sandstone for grinding; in the next bay is a lead wheel and in the next a small brush. The picture shows the large flywheels which were used to turn the lathes

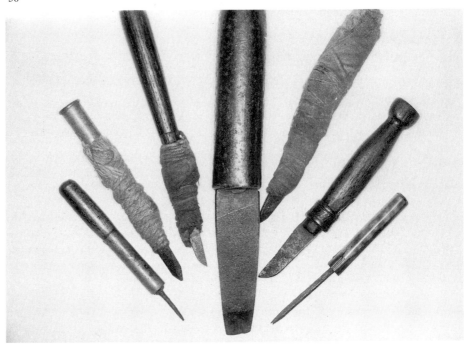

Figure 4.27 Joe Lyth's home-made hand carving tools

Figure 4.28 A page from Joe Lyth's pattern book with two of his hand tools, an ivory marker and three bar brooches made by him

required for that particular ornament. If it was to be carved, the worker would use his own simple, hand-made tools which might have been fashioned from an old file or piece of hacksaw blade, with a handle of leather wrapped around an old clothes peg or cartridge case (*Figure 4.27*). The tools looked very crude, but they were precious, sometimes being handed down from father to son. With these rough implements the craftsman could fashion the most delicate designs, sometimes with a sketch in front of him, often with the design only in his head (*Figure 4.28*).

The next process was leading, which involved polishing the piece on a lead wheel to remove the scores and grinding marks made by the sandstone wheel and, in the case of a brooch for example, to give a flat base. The piece was held against the flat side of the lead wheel which again was home-made (*Figure 4.29*). Some lead was

Figure 4.29 J. W. Barker leading

melted in an old frying pan with a little antimony and tin around a central wooden stake. When cold, the lead was mounted on a lathe and, while turning at speed, would be shaped with a cold chisel or a piece of glass until it was about 20 mm thick tapering to a knife edge.

The leading was done wet with the aid of a little rotten stone or tripoli, a finely abrasive river mud of a creamy white colour which came from Derbyshire. The rotten stone was contained in an old tin tray under the wheel and a splashguard, which might be made from an old trouser leg, hung over the front of the wheel. All cutting was done with the edge of the lead wheel.

When the piece required drilling, a lathe was used fitted with a diamond shaped bit, or even an old umbrella spoke which seemed to be even more successful than a conventional bit. The articles were usually carved first and then drilled, a delicate operation, because if the piece cracked much time and effort had been wasted (*Figure 4.30*).

Figure 4.30 Pieces of jet in various stages of manufacture

The final process was polishing on a succession of wheels which were called 'boards'. Only the first of these, a pig's bristle brush, was called a brush. The listing board, which came next, was again home-made. It consisted of 25 mm strips of wool, usually cut from old woollen garments, wound tightly around a wooden core. With both these boards rotten stone and water were used to give the first polish. Then the article had to be carefully washed to remove all traces of the rotten stone and dried in a box of sawdust.

The final high polish was given on a series of boards of walrus hide, porpoise hide or leather, or using a rouge wheel which was a soft brush of pure hair. With these boards they used a mixture of jeweller's rouge and oil called 'copperas'. This gave the article as well as the workers a reddish hue which earned the latter the nickname, the Red Demons! Copperas was later replaced by a mixture of lampblack, paraffin and linseed oil which brought out the deep black, velvety lustre of the jet. A final polish on a shag board, a wheel of chamois leather with shaggy edges, and the craftsman's work was done.

Figure 4.31 The beading board

Now the women took over, threading the beads on a beading board (*Figure 4.31*), affixing the backs to brooches, mounting on cards and pricing. The hooks and fasteners usually came from Birmingham and were nearly always of base metal. Gold and silver were seldom used except as decoration on more expensive items.

In the larger jet shops the articles made covered the whole range of jewellery and ornaments that are described in Chapter 5. The men who worked alone usually concentrated on a particular field. Some specialized in carving, some in engraving and others in inlay work. They were often known by their speciality; thus some were known as 'furniture men' or 'cameo men'. Others became noted for one particular product, for example Thomas Ross was known for his very fine pen-holders and Tom Ellewell for bracelets. It is sad that now so few of these men are remembered because of the absence of any written records.

The decline of the industry

The peak years of the Victorian jet industry fell between 1870 and 1874. Over 1000 men were employed in the business and one can only imagine what it must have been like to live in this small seaside town at this time. There was full employment and affluence. Everywhere the wheels were turning at full capacity, while every shop was filled with this gleaming black jewellery. Perhaps it looked a little sombre and some of the more critical observers of the day commented on its funereal aspect, saying with some scorn that 'even the dogs are black'. But the mood of the local people must surely have been anything but black. They could only see the enormous demand for their product from all over the world and the export figure for 1874 of £100 000 would be equivalent to about £1 million today. There could have been no thought in their minds then that within just one decade the industry would have fallen into such a decline that the *Whitby Gazette* of 1884, speaking of the trade, said 'at no period in its history has it been at such a low ebb'. The paper added: 'only 300 men are still employed in the trade'.

When the recession came it hit the independent workers first. The larger manufacturers were able to keep going for some time by cutting back on their workforces. Many returned to a trade which they had followed before starting as jet manufacturers. James Ainsley for example (*Figure 4.12*) returned to his old trade as a corn merchant. Many of the top-paid craftsmen had earned so much in the peak years that they had sufficient money to open a shop or a boarding house when there was no longer a demand for their skills. By 1921 there were only 40 men still working in the trade, in 1936 there were five and after the Second World War there were just three left. When they died the Victorian jet industry came to an end.

What brought about such a rapid change of fortune? Why was it that over a period of about 50 years this jewel went from being probably the most popular in Britain to being completely neglected, unworn and unwanted? Surely no other gemstone in the world has undergone such a rapid fluctuation in its popularity as has jet. Fashion played a big part, of course. Any jewel has its periods of being in or out of fashion; one might mention the Bohemian garnet or the opal. But none has ever been so completely rejected as was jet in the middle of the 20th century. In the 1950s one could buy a carrier bag full of jet jewellery for 2s 6d (12p) and it was only in the late 1970s and early 1980s that jet was once again regarded as anything but repulsive.

There are very many reasons for its downfall, but one of the most instantly recognizable was its association with mourning. The very cause of the industry's boost in 1861 was responsible for its rejection in the next century. The Boer war, followed by the two World Wars, made the British people anxious to avoid any reminder of death. In any case the custom of wearing black for mourning was gradually disappearing, so that today only Royalty adopt the full regalia of mourning demanded by tradition. Nowadays grief does not have to be visibly demonstrated by wearing clothes of a particular style or colour. Now black is merely a smart fashion colour, a fact which has allowed jet at last to drop its morbid association with mourning and once more become recognized as the beautiful jewel it has been since prehistoric times.

Although the connection with mourning may account for the unpopularity of jet in the 20th century, it does not explain the rapid decline of the industry in the late 19th century. Other more immediate reasons must be sought. One of these must be the change in ladies' fashions. The crinoline lasted only a very short time and its unwieldiness soon gave way to a much slimmer and more streamlined look in the 1880s and 1890s. Thus the need for large jewellery also declined. Colours in fashion also changed from the dark reds and purples of the mid-century to lighter and brighter tones. The 1890s were known as the 'naughty nineties', when the mood was changing from the seriousness of the Victorians towards the gayer Edwardian society. This was also the period of Art Nouveau, in which jewellery was light and fanciful, and bright colours and designs were more important than the jewels themselves. In 1886 Queen Victoria celebrated her Golden Jubilee, and at last was persuaded to relinquish the full mourning she had worn since the death of Prince Albert 25 years before.

Dame Fashion then was the first to toll the knell of the jet industry, but there were internal problems within the industry itself which did nothing to help it resist this unavoidable external pressure. First there was the seeming inability of the craftsmen to adapt to changing fashion. In 1947 a reviewer wrote: 'the basis of the work appears to have been the designer-craftsman. Now that may be all very well if the craftsman *is* a designer. There were however too few of these and the work became tradition bound' (Walker, 1947). This last phrase seemed to describe perfectly the attitude of the industry. Jewellery which was appropriate in Queen Victoria's days must still be acceptable in the new century. But such attitudes are the cause of stagnation in many industries. 'What was good enough for my father and his father before him is good enough for me.' How often has this sentiment led to dull repetitious work in any field.

In the 1920s Art Deco jewellery made full use of the black and white theme, yet there is no indication that the jet workers capitalized on this. Jet combined with ivory in a geometrical design would have fitted in well with the prevailing fashion. However, the same old designs of flowers, fruit and foliage were still coming from Whitby. The jewellery had become so unpopular by the 1930s that most of the jet workers were concentrating on small souvenirs for holiday-makers. Although attractive in their own way, these could never bring the world-wide demand that the fine jewellery had enjoyed.

The industry had another problem. When working at full capacity there was a desperate shortage of good hard jet. Finding jet by mining could not be related to demand. It was, by nature of jet's geological distribution, a hit-and-miss operation. So the industry started using local soft jet. This led to disastrous results as expensive ornaments began to crack and break up during wear or even when exposed to heat or sunlight in a shop window. In an effort to increase supplies, jet was imported from France and Spain from 1869 onwards. Notwithstanding the fact that excellent hard jet does occur in Spain, it appears that much that was imported into England was of the soft variety. It was extremely difficult to recognize the soft jet in the rough, and so many workers were probably ignorant of the fact that they were using it until after it had been worked and its defects began to show.

This again illustrates the lack of any organized quality control in the industry. This was a serious omission, especially when demand began to fall. Neither was there any price control. Individual workers would buy their rough jet and sell their products quite independently, which resulted in a complete lack of co-ordination in both price and quality.

In 1890 some of the bigger manufacturers belatedly got together to try to rectify this state of affairs. Led by I. Langdale, Stephen Feran, Charles Bryan and their secretary Godfrey Hirst, they organized the Whitby Jet Operatives Association. They agreed to bring out a trade mark which guaranteed the quality of the jet as follows:

No. A1 Genuine Whitby hard jet
No. 1 Foreign hard jet

TO VISITORS.
GUARANTEED AND MARKED
WHITBY JET JEWELLERY.

All articles bearing this TRADE MARK & stamped A1 quality, are of the finest English Jet from the Whitby mines.

Without it, purchasers are liable to be defrauded by paying an exorbitant price for a comparatively worthless article made from foreign soft Jet.

Owing to the ruinous effect the introduction of Foreign Jet has had upon the Whitby Jet Trade, large meetings of influential members of the trade, presided over by E. W. Beckett, Esq., M.P., were held at Whitby in 1890, to discuss and devise some method whereby all goods sold as Jet should have their proper classification as to quality, and so that purchasers should have some substantial guarantee—(by the marking of goods) as to the quality of Jet they bought, the result of the meeting being that several of the leading Manufacturers decided to adopt a system of classification of the different qualities of Jet and give a substantial guarantee, by each article bearing the Manufacturer's Registered Trade Mark.

The classification decided upon is as follows :—

No. A1.—Genuine Whitby Hard Jet.

No. 1.—Foreign Hard Jet.

No. 2.—Soft Jet.

Only the No. A1 and No. 1 will show the Trade Mark.

The first firm that publicly undertook to give such guarantee for Genuine Whitby Jet was that of

I. LANGDALE, "Standard Jet Works,"

Whose goods may be had retail in Whitby from the appointed Sole Agents only, viz:—

MISS RODGERS, Fancy Bazaar, Skinner Street,

MESSRS. HORNE & SON, "Gazette" Office.

(a)

(b)

(c)

Figure 4.32 (a) The trade mark which was introduced in 1890. (b) An example of its uses. (c) The trade mark on a small brass plate fixed to the inside of a bracelet

No. 2 Soft jet.

Only A1 and 1 were to show the trade mark (*Figure 4.32*).

Many retailers who had given up stocking jet jewellery now agreed to take it up again on these conditions. Furthermore a Valuation Committee to fix the price for the public was to be instituted. The committee was also to look into the variety of the goods made to bring them more in line with the public taste.

   In spite of these good intentions the scheme had little success. This was partly a result of changing fashion, but must also have been due to the lack of co-operation from the small and independent jet workers. In the end the effort was in vain and the decline continued.

   A further contributory factor not yet mentioned but possibly the one that had the greatest impact was the advent of imitations. As with any successful product of any age, jet jewellery no sooner became established than imitations of all types appeared on the market. Vulcanite – invented as early as 1846 (see Chapter 7) – black glass and later bakelite were so much cheaper to produce that they could compete unfairly with the hand-made and more expensive jet items. There was no Trade Descriptions Act and no doubt many simulants were sold under the guise of 'Genuine Whitby Jet'. Even when the imitations were not designed to deceive, the cheaper price made them more attractive to all but the most discerning. Thus the sale of true jet became more and more confined to Whitby itself.

   Now as the wheel of fashion turns yet again and black is once again becoming a fashionable colour for accessories, jet is enjoying a well-deserved revival. Grandmother's old jet necklace is taken down from the attic, dusted off, and eagerly sought after both by antique collectors and the fashionable young ladies who have discovered it for the first time.

The present day

After the Second World War there were just three trained craftsmen left in Whitby, William Cox, Wilfred Braithwaite and Joe Lyth. Jet was at the lowest ebb of its popularity and these men kept their business going by making and selling small souvenirs for tourists. No young men were interested in the trade. It was to be another 30 years before jet jewellery came back into fashion, but by then it was too late. All three of the men with their Victorian tradition had died and there was no one left to teach the craft to those who now wished to learn it. Today's jet workers are therefore self taught (*Figure 4.33*). None has the skills of the old jet men and none can produce the work of a Speedy, a Greenbury or a Snowdon.

Figure 4.33 The author watching Alec Mackenzie working jet in Whitby

Figure 4.34 Some examples of modern jet jewellery by Alec Mackenzie. Ivory and amber are combined with jet for contrast

Antique jet jewellery is in great demand and today commands a high price. The most popular of the old pieces are the earrings which, in their never-ending variety, are so very beautiful that nothing made today can compare with them. In the mid-1980s beads suddenly came into fashion again and the intricately carved jet beads were in demand. Today the jet jewellery made in Whitby is plainer and simpler than that made in the 19th century, but perhaps it is more in keeping with modern fashion (*Figure 4.34*). In this day and age when time is money, no one could possibly spend the long hours needed to make the detailed and intricate jewellery that the Victorians made. If modern workers charged for their time, the price of each article would be astronomical. For this reason the 19th century jewellery which survives is unique and irreplaceable. It is only lately that its value has become appreciated once more since it is at last recognized that in all probability nothing of its kind will ever be made again.

Repair and preservation

Articles of jet jewellery should always be kept separate from metal and stone jewellery which are harder and will scratch the jet.

Jet may be safely washed in warm, soapy water and cleaned with an old, soft toothbrush. After rinsing well and drying, a little oil rubbed into the surface will help to restore its shine. Although collectors prefer necklaces to be on their original thread, for wearing it is safer to rethread them on a strong, black thread. Bracelets can be rethreaded using hat elastic or, when the holes are too small, two or four thicknesses of shirring elastic may be used. If the surface of the jet is lightly scratched through wear, it can be repolished using a little Brasso on a soft cloth. Deep scratches can only be removed by professional polishing.

References

ANON, *The official catalogue of the Great Exhibition of the works of industry of all nations.* Spicer Bros. W. Clowes and Sons, London (1851)

BEDE, THE VENERABLE, *A History of the English Church and People,* Penguin Edn., 1956

BOWER, J. A., 'Whitby jet and its manufacture,' *Journal of the Society of Arts,* **XXII,** No. 1100 (1873)

FLETCHER, J. S., *Picturesque History of Yorkshire,* Blackwood, London (1901)

HUNT, R., 'The Whitby jet and Ammonite ornaments,' *The Art Journal* (1856)

KENDALL, H. P., *The streets of Whitby,* Whitby Literary and Philosophical Society Publication (1976)

KENDALL, H. P., *The story of Whitby jet,* Whitby Literary and Philosophical Society Publication (1977)

LINSKILL, M., 'Pictures from Whitby,' *In Good Words,* 38 (1885)

PEERS, SIR C. and RALEGH RADFORD, C. A., 'The Saxon Monastery of Whitby,' *Archaeologia,* **89,** (1943)

RODWAY, E. *Whitby in 1851,* private publication, printed by Ebor Press, York

SIMPSON, M., 'Whitby jet and jet ornaments,' *The Art Journal* (1869)

SCOTT, SIR W., *Marmion,* Macmillan, London (1909)

STOKER, B., *Dracula,* 16th Edn., Rider, London (1927)

TAYLOR, L., *Mourning Dress,* George Allen and Unwin (1983)

WALKER, A. B., 'The death of black amber,' *Yorkshire Life,* Vol. 1., No. 5 (1947)

WOODWARK, T. H., *The rise and fall of the Whitby jet trade,* Whitby Literary and Philosophical Society Publication (1922)

YOUNG, THE REV. G. *A History of Whitby,* Clark and Medd, London (1817)

Chapter 5

The jewellery

The bottom clear,
Now laid with many a set,
of seed pearls, ere she bath'd her there,
Was known as black as jet.

Drayton

Problems of dating

It is not easy to date jet jewellery with any precision. A rough guide may be obtained by comparing jet pieces with other items of jewellery whose dates are known, but some designs were made in jet for many years after they had gone out of fashion in other jewellery. A very rough indication of the date of a piece is given by its size. Very large pieces of jewellery were worn in the mid-19th century with the crinoline, and the size tended to decrease as the century progressed. In gold and silver jewellery certain themes can be used to date pieces to within one decade and these themes can be used as a guide to the dating of jet, although one must always bear in mind that the men of the Whitby jet industry were reluctant to change as fashion changed.

The designs

Designs that were popular in the early days from about 1837 to 1850 were knots, serpents, vine leaves, grapes, hazel nuts, twigs and branching coral. Very long earrings and long jet chains were also worn in that period. From 1850 to 1860, as well as those patterns already in use, flowers became popular. Most of these had some sentimental meaning, either of affection, mourning or piety. For example, fern meant sincerity, lily of the valley represented the return of happiness, roses stood for love and forget me not for true love. There were the obvious symbols of good luck such as shamrocks and horseshoes; these were frequently made with opening pointing downwards, contrary to the popular superstition which says that the shoe must point upwards 'to hold the luck in'. Clasped hands showed friendship and affection, and love birds, hearts and flowers and lovers' knots all clearly indicated love.

On the more sombre side were willow and yew, both of which denoted sorrow, and convolvulus, which stood for eternal sleep. Religious themes were expressed by crosses and crucifixes, and mourning by a hand holding a wreath. Faith, hope and charity were represented by a cross, an anchor and a heart, respectively (*Figure*

66

Fig. 5.1 : A large brooch of the
mid-19th century, bearing
the cross, heart and
anchor representing faith,
hope and charity.
Width 63 mm
Total length 158 mm

Figure 5.2 A cross with the initials I.H.S., a mourning locket with the initials I.O.M. and a hair
compartment on the reverse and a locket with the initials A.E.I. Size of cross, 62 × 102 mm

5.1). As well as thematic designs, engraved initials or monograms cut in fine fretwork showed the initials I.M.O. (in memory of), I.H.S. (the name of Jesus) or A.E.I. (amity, eternity, infinity) (*Figure 5.2*). A very popular line was the MIZPAH brooch. This refers to a quotation from Genesis 31:49, 'The Lord watch between me and thee when we are absent, one from another' (*Figure 5.3*). Personal monograms are also found.

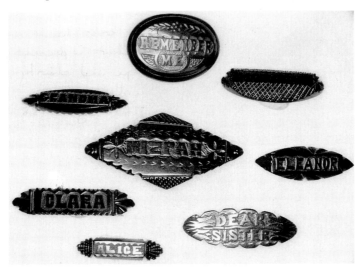

Figure 5.3 Typical souvenir brooches made throughout the 19th century and well into the 20th. Width of 'Mizpah' brooch, 68 mm

From 1860 to 1870 jewellery combining jet with other, often coloured, centres was favoured. These included shell cameos, ivory, mosaics, pietra dura and miniatures painted on porcelain (*Figure 5.4* and colour plates). The porcelain plaques which are frequently found set as brooches, earrings and pendants were hand painted in Italy. The most common are the Green Boy, a boy wearing a green hat, the Blue Boy and a Shepard Boy. Apparently each family painted only one picture. In the later part of the century, from about 1875 to 1890, brooches were smaller and the bar brooch was universally popular. Such a wealth of design and variety can be found in these small brooches that it is rare to find two alike (*Figures 5.5* and *4.21*). All the usual motives were used, such as flowers, leaves and hearts and there was a big trade in name brooches. Particularly in demand were the sort of brooches beloved by the Victorians, engraved with the words Mother, Grandma or Baby. These were popular and inexpensive gifts (*Figure 5.3*).

Having suggested that the majority of the jet workers were rather repetitive in their work, one must say in all fairness that there were the exceptional craftsmen, the true artists, who produced individual and original designs which were often highly complicated. When they can still be found, such articles illustrate well the difference between the ordinary 'jettie', who turned out large numbers of stereotyped designs, and the sometimes brilliant craftsmen whose work showed true artistic ability and inventiveness (*Figure 5.6*).

Figure 5.4 A selection of brooches combining jet with colourful centres including a miniature portrait painted on porcelain, shell cameos, ivory and pietra dura. Size of centre cameo brooch 58 × 68 mm

Figure 5.5 A selection of bar brooches illustrating the detailed carving and infinite variety of the small objects. Length of brooches 48–52 mm

Figure 5.6 Close up of the bust of Mary Queen of Scots shown in *Figure 4.22* which illustrates the fine workmanship of the artist–craftsman. Height of bust without pedestal 60 mm (shown approximately actual size)

Figure 5.7 Examples of the work of Geoffrey Hirst in the 1890s. The design is cut out of the jet and the surrounding area is painted either yellow or blue. Width of largest brooch, 46 mm

Figure 5.8 Commemorative jewellery for Queen Victoria's 50th and 60th anniversaries in 1887 and 1897. Whitby Abbey and the town crest, a souvenir from a military camp in North Yorkshire and in the centre a membership badge of an unknown order or society. Width of centre brooch, 48 mm

Godfrey Hirst was one of the few jet workers to try some new techniques. Parkin reports in 1882 that Mr Hirst was experimenting with enamelling on jet. Since no items have ever been seen of this nature one assumes that it was not successful. However, he was successful with another of his innovations. He cut away the jet to leave the design outstanding and then painted around the design with a yellow or blue paint. Quite a few examples of this technique are still to be found (*Figure 5.7*).

Sometimes jewellery was especially commissioned to a private order. Thus one comes across a special design such as the brooch in *Figure 5.8* saying 'member Jones' or the paper knife (*Figure 5.38*) which was made for Polly Rhodes in 1882.

Commemorative jewellery was made to celebrate important events such as Queen Victoria's Jubilee (*Figure 5.8*). One exciting event in Whitby was the sinking of the hospital ship Rohilla in 1914. The jet industry was then still sufficiently active to produce brooches commemorating this event (*Figure 5.9*).

Beads

Probably the most popular items of jet jewellery were strings of beads. These varied in length from 500 mm to the very long 1500 mm. The former was known as a

Figure 5.9 A brooch bearing a photograph of General Gordon, two military buttons and a souvenir of the sinking of the Hospital Ship Rohilla in the First World War. Width of the Gordon brooch, 30 mm

necklace while the long row was known as a 'guard'. The beads were basically of three types: plain, faceted and carved. There were many variations on these themes, and all three types could be combined in one necklace.

Before the 19th century, all jet carving was done without the use of a lathe. *Figure 5.10* shows a typical necklace, dating from about 1760. The large, rather crude beads are somewhat flattened. When the lathe was introduced, perfectly round beads could be made. The beads varied in size from very small, 2.5 mm, to some very large ones of 40 mm in diameter. Jet workers who made beads worked nothing else and were naturally called 'bead men'. They were employed by the owner of the jet shop and took their orders from the foreman. John Hill was a bead man who worked in Mr Trattle's shop in about 1900. He never went to school and could neither read nor write. He was paid 17 shillings (85p) for a four-day week of 12 hours a day.

In making beads the general method of jet working as described in Chapter 4 was followed. Often the poorer quality jet or offcuts were used. After the skin had been removed the beads were chopped out across the grain in squares. After being

Figure 5.10 A very early necklace *circa* 1780, in which the beads are hand made without the use of a lathe and are double threaded. Diameter of one bead, 25 mm

cornered or 'cushioned' the beads were shaped and drilled. At this stage they were called 'dullies'. Plain beads then only needed to pass through the various stages of polishing. Faceted and carved beads required a great deal more work.

Faceting was called 'canting' by the Whitby jet workers. The facets or 'cants' were put on by holding the beads against a revolving lead wheel (*Figure 4.29*). Since the beads were held in the hand, jet turners often had bandaged fingers! The facets were put on starting at the drill hole and then in rows up the bead to the girdle and down the other side to the drill hole. The facets might be triangular (dog tooth), four-sided or five-sided. The more facets on the bead the better. Some workers were able to put 120 facets on one bead, all by rule of thumb and a good eye. Very small beads which could not be held in the hand were stuck onto a dop while being worked. This was done with ockamatutt, called 'tut' for short, which was the jet workers' special glue. The origin of the name is lost, but it was a mixture of Collins glue and shellac which was bought in solid sticks and had to be melted down before use (see *Figure 4.15*). The tut was used for applying pins to brooches, joining halves of chain links or any other work which required glueing.

Carved beads were known as 'cut and shaded' beads and were commonly of two main designs, the rose and the fern. In *Figure 5.11* combinations of these patterns can be seen. All the cutting was done on a lead wheel. All these designs and more can still be found today in antique shops. They may be in single rows or combined into double or triple rows. A favourite Victorian design was a combination of a single strand passing round the back of the neck which widened into two or three

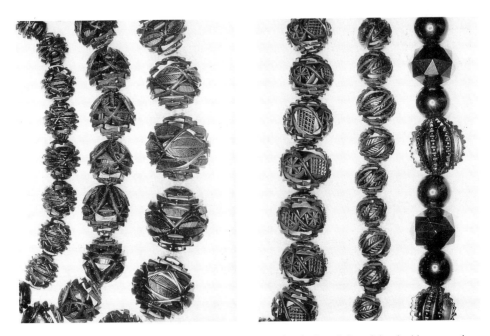

Figure 5.11 Examples of the most common designs found in beads; from left to right, double rose and fern, rose and fern, double rose with fern centre, double rose with decorated centre, fern and a combination of plain, faceted and watermelon beads. Diameter of beads, 12–25 mm

strands in the front (*Figure 5.12*). These recall the design of the Bronze Age crescentic necklaces, both in their construction and in the use of spacer plates. Often the poor quality Spanish jet was used for such necklaces and they may be found today in a distressed state showing the cracking which so often occurred in soft jet (*Figure 1.3*). This type of jet was referred to in Whitby as 'nattled jet' and the cracks were known as 'nattles'. The soft jet, whatever its origin, was known as French jet. This had no connection with either its provenance or the black glass later called French jet. To the Victorian jet worker the word French was an insult used to describe something of no value or of poor quality. Another term for such jet was 'bastard jet'. One must remember that at the beginning of the 19th century England had been at war with France for many years.

The beads were usually threaded by women using a wooden bead board (*Figure 4.31*). On this eight grooves were marked out in different lengths. The beads were

Figure 5.12 A typical faceted necklace with one strand fastening at the neck passing through a spacer plate into three graduated rows in the front

Figure 5.13 Examples of fasteners. On the left are tubular snap fasteners, down the centre various hooks, on the top right end plates through which ribbons were threaded and on the lower right a snap fastener for a three strand necklace

placed into the grooves for correct grading. In the early Victorian times they were threaded on a very narrow ribbon and later on silk cord. The ribbon or cord was passed through a piece of piano wire which was then bent, twisted and threaded through the beads and the fastener. To secure the ribbon it was knotted and then passed back through the last four or five beads and sewn with a few stitches.

The original fasteners were often made from a tubular snap fastener fitted into two matching beads (*Figure 5.13*). Sometimes the larger necklaces were fastened with a hook and ring. Some necklaces ended on each side with a plate in which a hole had been made so that a ribbon could be sewn on to it. The necklace was then fastened by the ribbon enabling the length to be adjusted. An interesting type of fastener is seen in *Figure 5.29* where the length can again be adjusted by the elastic.

There is no accurate method of dating beads, since the same designs were made throughout the period. It is, however, possible to surmise that the larger necklaces were worn in the mid-century.

Brooches

Brooches were made throughout the 19th century and well into the 20th. They were made in an infinite variety of shape, style and decoration. Other than the simplest, plain styles it is unusual to find two exactly alike. The majority were made in two parts, a plainer backing and a more elaborately carved front piece which was glued onto the backing. The latter made a frame or border for the front part but in itself it could be a wide variety of designs. It could be plain, milled, faceted or carved. The front of the brooch could be any one of innumerable designs.

In the early days of the industry the theme of the decoration was usually taken from nature. Flowers, fruit and foliage were predominant and very elaborate combinations of these three were carved in high relief. Later the jet carvers were criticized for their lack of originality and some of the larger manufacturers approached the *London Art Journal* for assistance in suggesting new designs. Unfortunately, the artists were not accustomed to designing for jet and the patterns they produced, which would have been suitable for gold or silver, did not lend themselves to a fragile material which had to be hand carved. Nevertheless, the more skilled of the jet craftsmen began to design their own jewellery and they produced ideas other than those suggested by nature.

One popular line developed was the carving of cameos. For this purpose some of the experienced shell cameo carvers from Naples were invited to Whitby to instruct the jet carvers in their art. For this reason all the early cameos are of traditional mythical subjects such as Greek and Roman gods, as are frequently found on shell cameos. The jet had to be treated rather differently to the shell and the cameos were executed in a higher relief and for this reason were able to show a more elaborate carving technique. Later the more experienced jet carvers began to carve the likenesses of well known figures of the day. Politicians, authors and well-known personalities were portrayed on brooches, pendants or in small statuettes (*Figure 5.14*). For the right fee a wealthy person could have his own likeness carved in cameo on a brooch or tie pin. E. H. Greenbury, John Speedy, W. Stonehouse, George Tyson and W. Lund were well-known cameo carvers. Examples of their work may be seen in Whitby museum.

The pins of brooches were always made of base metal. Very early brooches, possibly made before 1830, had large pins set into the jet (*Figure 5.15a and b*). Such brooches are often of crude workmanship and may have been made entirely by hand. In the 19th century there were no safety catches and the end of the pins extended beyond the edge of the brooch. The pins were glued in place using ockamatutt.

Figure 5.14 One classical head cameo, one of Charles Dickens and one of Disraeli. Size of the Dickens cameo, 33 × 41 mm (shown approximately actual size)

Figure 5.15 The front and reverse views of a very early brooch, showing the type of pin which was inlaid into the jet. Diameter of brooch, 71 mm

Pendants

Pendants were made in the same wide variety as brooches and the two often came in matching sets and were worn together. They could be worn on a ribbon or as an integral part of a necklace. Lockets became fashionable about 1870, usually opening to show two or sometimes four glass covered compartments. Some had a carved jet front with only a single glass compartment at the back. Lockets were very popular as betrothal gifts, both for men, who wore them on a watch chain, and for women. The large number of lockets that have survived to the present day reflect the romantic and sentimental nature of the Victorians. The lockets normally had a photograph on one side and a lock of hair on the other (*Figure 5.16*). There is

Figure 5.16 The inside of a locket used as a token of affection. Note the plain undecorated jet which distinguishes it from the vulcanite copy which is invariably highly decorated (*Figure 7.12*)

no space in this book to discuss hair jewellery, but it must be stressed that hair ornaments were not always mourning jewellery. They were often tokens of affection and the young Victorian ladies learnt the art of coiling or plaiting the hair into attractive arrangements. Sometimes the hair of two people would be combined, such as the hair of mother and daughter or of two lovers. Queen Victoria's 16th birthday present from her mother was a brooch made from her mother's hair.

Hair was used in mourning jewellery too, and such articles can usually be recognized by the use of the initials I.M.O. (in memory of) on the front of the locket. Usually the hair was arranged in a simple criss-cross pattern in mourning jewellery and in a more elaborate fashion in the love tokens (*Figure 5.17*). In these the hair was often curled and decorated with gold wire and small seed pearls.

It is important to note that in jet lockets the inside is always plain and undecorated and underneath the glass compartment the jet is left in a rough state and unpolished. This fact is useful in distinguishing jet lockets from their imitations.

Pendants and brooches were sometimes inlaid with mother-of-pearl. To do this the inlay was cut out, laid on the jet and outlined. This area was then cut out until the mother-of-pearl fitted exactly into it. Using ockamatutt, the inlay was glued

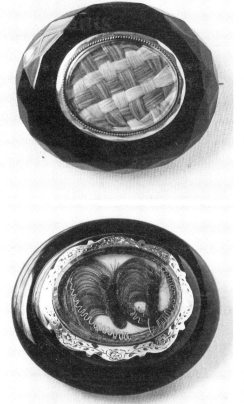

Figure 5.17 Two hair brooches *circa* 1870 and the reverse of the upper one. The ~~top~~ lower brooch is a token of affection, the ~~lower~~ top, a mourning brooch. Width of brooches, 57 mm and 53 mm

into place and the glue was spread right over the inlay and the jet and allowed to set. When dry, the piece was polished off and the glue, which had set into the grooves on the inlay, outlined the design.

Crosses were made in all the traditional shapes and designs. Some were small and plain, others large and elaborately carved or engraved (*Figure 5.2*). They were worn on a jet chain or a ribbon. Some of the larger crosses were probably hung on the wall rather than worn.

Earrings

When attempting to date earrings, a rough guide can be the size; thus very large earrings were popular in the first half of the 19th century and they tended to get smaller in the second half. In the 1850s and 1860s Creole earrings were fashionable. An encyclopaedia of 1906 defines an earring as: 'an ornament, consisting of a plain ring or loop to which a pendant is attached, suspended from the lobe of the ear, which is bored for the purpose.' This describes the Victorian earrings very well. Almost all were of the drop type, whether they were small bells or acorns or long drops which could be up to 75 mm long (*Figure 5.18*). Small stud earrings were only made in the 20th century. The variety of design in the Victorian earrings encompassed the whole range of the jet carver's art. Milling, faceting, carving and inlaying may be found or any combination of these techniques. As with brooches, jet was used as a background for cameos, shell cameos, porcelain paintings or ammonites, and it was common to find earrings and brooch to match (*Figure 5.19*).

Figure 5.18 A selection of jet earrings showing the immense variety and the different methods of attachment to the hook. Length of large earring, 106 mm

Figure 5.19 A demi-parure of jet and shell cameos

Figure 5.20 This illustrates the two common methods of attachment of the hook to the earring. Long drops usually had a bell cap fitting. The cameo earring shows the many parts of which it is made

Earrings were usually made in four sections (*Figure 5.20*). The main drop or body of the earring was attached to the wire by a ring and shackle. The shackle was a U-shaped piece through which a black-headed pin passed to secure the drop. The name is a relic of the old sailing industry which in the early days co-existed with the jet industry. In the smaller earrings the drop was attached directly to the wire. Base metal fittings were used and all the earrings had wire loops. There were no screws, clips or studs until the 20th century. Being hand made, the two members of a pair of earrings were not always exactly the same size. Just the tiniest difference can sometimes be seen, but it was said in Whitby that to the old jet workers any two of anything made a pair! However, such was the immense variety of earrings made that in the present day it is well nigh impossible to find a matching earring if one of a pair is lost.

Rings

Rings were made of jet but it was not a suitable substance, being too brittle to stand up to the wear to which rings are normally subjected. They were rather fragile and very few have survived to the present day.

Bracelets

Bracelets were worn throughout the period, usually in pairs, but sometimes in larger numbers (*Figure 5.21*). Basically there were two types; those that were made from two solid pieces of jet, pinned and glued together, and those that were segmented. The solid bracelets were very fragile and few have survived. The segmented bracelets, made of small sections threaded on elastic, were more popular and may still be found in fairly large numbers. As with the other jewellery, the bracelets illustrate all aspects of the jet carver's art. In the early period strap-and-buckle types were fashionable, either made entirely of jet or with silver or gold buckle fittings. This is one of the infrequent examples of precious metals being used with jet jewellery.

Figure 5.21 A selection of bracelets of the plano-convex type strung on elastic. Total length of bracelets, from 175–205 mm

The bracelets of a more simple design were made of sections which had a plano-convex cross-section. The more elaborate ones had pieces which were concave-convex so that the curvature of the bracelet fitted the arm. During manufacture, the bracelets were cemented together to form a complete hoop to ensure accuracy of workmanship. They were then separated for drilling and threading. Before being drilled the ends of each adjoining piece were numbered so that they would be threaded in the correct position. Since many of the workers were illiterate, marks were used, either dots or lines, instead of numbers. In the end piece the drill holes were larger than average so that the knot in the elastic could be concealed (*Figure 5.22*).

Figure 5.22 A segmented bracelet made of curved pieces with rope borders. The centre piece is a cameo of William Shakespeare. Size of centre piece, 46 × 53 mm

Serpents have been a popular subject for jewellery since Ancient Greek times; they were supposed to represent eternal life. The serpent sometimes had a heart (symbolizing love) suspended from its jaws. Snake bracelets were in fashion throughout the Victorian period. In the late 1870s they were very large, having up to nine coils, and were worn over the gloves. Each section of the snake was angled at both ends so that, when the threading elastic was pulled tight, the snake coiled (*Figure 5.23*).

Just as today copper bracelets are worn as a 'cure' for rheumatism, so in the 19th century jet bracelets were worn, probably with as little effect.

Figure 5.23 A typical snake bracelet with carved head and tail and faceted body. Length of snake extended, 445 mm, width of head, 15 mm

Necklaces

A jet necklace could be plain and simple or complicated and highly decorated. The only limiting factors were the artistic ability and technical skill of the jet worker. There were three basic types, the fringe necklace, the collarette and the chain with one or more pendants.

Figure 5.24 A fringe necklace of plain half beads and plain and carved drops. Length, 425 mm, diameter of largest bead, 19 mm

Fringe necklaces (*Figure 5.24*) consisted of beads flattened on one side and convex on the other. From these beads small round beads were suspended on articulated wires. The flat beads could be plain, faceted or carved in any of the usual designs and the pendant beads could vary in the same way. These necklaces had a tubular snap fastener set into a matching bead which formed an integral part of the necklace.

Collarettes (*Figure 5.25*) were made of flattened elliptical pieces of jet, each drilled twice and shaped so that one end was slightly wider than the other. Thus

Figure 5.25 A typical faceted collarette and how it could be worn close to the neck or on the dress

Figure 5.26 A chain and drop necklace (*left*), and (*right*) an example of how it was worn over a dress *circa* 1890. Length of necklace, 505 mm

when they were threaded the pieces lay flat. Collarettes usually had at each end a loop made of jet through which a ribbon was fitted which was tied around the neck. As collarettes were usually worn close to the neck this method of fastening allowed them to be adjusted to any size. This type of necklace was popular in the 1880s and contemporary photographs show that they could be worn either close to the neck or over the dress.

The chain and pendant type of necklace was usually worn over the dress (*Figure 5.26*). Many combinations of different chains or patterns of pendants were made (*Figure 5.27*). There might be one, three, five or seven pendants which were suspended from the chain in three ways. The small drops, which were sometimes said to represent tears (*Figure 5.28*), were fixed by small articulated wires fitted

Figure 5.27 An example of a large and elaborate
chain and plate necklace with cameo drops.
Mid-19th century. Length of necklace, 660 mm,
centre pendant, 38 × 68 mm

Figure 5.28 A chain and drop necklace *circa* 1860.
The drops were said to represent tears. Length of
necklace 440 mm

Figure 5.29 This chain and drop necklace has an interesting fastener, carved to match the pendant and attached to the chain by elastic to allow the length to be adjusted. Length, 400 mm, pendant without loop, 46 × 54 mm

Figure 5.30 An early chain and drop necklace. Acorns and oakleaves were popular before 1850. Length, 430 mm, centre pendant, 60 mm

into drilled holes in the chain and in the drop. In the second type the pendants were fixed by shackles similar to those used in earrings (*Figure 5.27*). Finally the pendants could be fixed by rings or loops of jet which were cut asymmetrically in two places and then glued together (*Figures 5.29 and 5.30*).

Chains

In the first half of the 19th century long chains were worn. In 1854 the Queen of Bavaria is said to have ordered one 1500 mm long from Isaac Greenbury. The chains sometimes had a cross or an anchor suspended from them. Chains came in a variety of sizes and shapes. The links could be oval, round or square. They could be plain, faceted, milled or carved or any combination of these designs (*Figure 5.31*).

Figure 5.31 A selection of chains

Each alternate link was whole while the others were split on opposite sides and then pinned and glued together to make the chain (*Figure 5.32*).

Ladies wore them as watch chains, fastened at the neck of the dress either by a hook or by means of a jet brooch. The chain then hung down to below the waist and then turned up to a small pocket at the waist line where the watch was kept (*Figure 5.33*). There were no wrist watches before the 20th century. Men wore smaller chains or Alberts (named after the husband of Queen Victoria) which held the watch at one end and usually one or more small charms or a seal on the other (*Figure 5.34*).

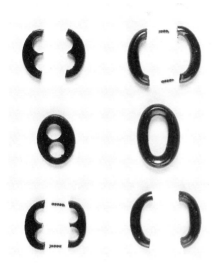

Figure 5.32 This illustrates the method of joining the alternate chain links by means of small twisted wires and glue

Figure 5.33 Left: A lady *circa* 1885 showing how the watch chain was worn. *Right:* A lady *circa* 1860 wearing large drop earrings, a pair of bracelets and a very long chain with a cross

Figure 5.34 A selection of gifts for gentlemen

Clothing

Jet decorations on dresses and capes consisted mainly of small faceted half beads (*Figure 5.35*). They were quickly superseded by 'French jet' (glass) which was cheaper and could be made into very small beads and tiny tubular beads called 'bugles'. These were often used as dress decoration in very large numbers.

Figure 5.35 A rare example of the use of jet beads to decorate clothing is seen on this belt

Figure 5.36 A selection of jet buttons. Some have two or three thread holes, others have metal loops on the reverse for sewing on to the clothes

Jet buttons were usually rather plain and drilled with two holes for the thread (*Figure 5.36*). They were occasionally decorated with paste or silver. Buckles were made with a thin layer of jet on a metal frame, while belts consisted of sections threaded on elastic in the same manner as bracelets.

In the late 19th and early 20th century very large hat pins were worn and the jet workers could use their imagination and creativity in this field.

Ornaments

As regards the variety of ornaments the only limit to what could be achieved was the skill of the craftsman. They made copies of Caedmon's cross, lighthouses, cigar holders and writing accessories. Miniature furniture was very popular (*Figure 5.37*). The furniture men mostly made small tables and chairs which were usually decorated with an engraving of Whitby Abbey. Sometimes the furniture was inlayed with mother-of-pearl or with an ammonite. For men there were cufflinks, shirt and collar studs, or small charms such as compasses, bibles or pigs and whistles (*Figure 5.34*).

The Victorian visitor to Whitby found such a large selection of souvenirs to choose from that there could hardly have been anyone who did not find the object of his choice. If he did fail to do so then he could have it especially made for him. In the early 20th century one lady, who came to Whitby every year for her holiday, had one or two small ornaments made for her on each visit. They were usually

Figure 5.37 A selection of miniature furniture, each piece decorated with an engraving of Whitby Abbey. Average height of tables, 65 mm, average height of chairs, 65 mm

made by Richard Storr whose shop still stands at the foot of the Abbey steps. This collection can be seen in the Whitby museum today.

The ammonites which are found in large numbers in the coastal cliffs around Whitby were frequently incorporated in both jewellery and ornaments (*Figure 5.38*). Small ammonites set in a carved jet surround made attractive brooches or tie

Figure 5.38 Typical souvenirs of the 19th century. The taper stand incorporates an ammonite; the paper knife was made in 1882 for Polly Rhodes. Length of paper knife, 148 mm

pins, and a small industry grew up alongside the jet industry for cutting and polishing these fossils.

Examples of all the jewellery and ornaments made in the 19th century may be found in antique shops today, but there were many years when there was no interest in jet. Between its heyday in the 1870s and its revival almost one hundred years later, jet jewellery lay gathering dust and was ignored by all but a few specialist collectors.

Chapter 6
Jet from other countries

And his face as white as ivory and his eyebrows black as jet

Mabinogion

Germany

In Germany the oldest finds of jet artifacts have been dated to the Stone Age period between 15 000 and 10 000 BC. Three important finds come from the area of the Upper Danube (Adam, 1978). The first was discovered in 1916 near the north west edge of the Swabian alps near Heubach. It was a small jet sculpture 38 cm long, which at first was thought to represent the segmented abdomen of a wasp (*Figure 6.1*). It now regarded as a representation of the larva of the dassel fly

Figure 6.1 An amulet in the form of an insect larva (38 mm long) found in Stone Age excavations in Germany (shown approximately actual size)

(*Oedemagena tarandi*). This fly parasitizes the reindeer and its larvae are found under the skin in very large numbers, over 1000 under a single skin. These larvae are still eaten today by the inland Eskimos of Northern Alaska and are regarded as a great delicacy. To the hunter-gatherers of the Stone Age the wearing of an amulet in the shape of the parasite of the reindeer would perhaps be a talisman to bring good fortune in their hunting. The reindeer was an important source not only of food but also of antlers, which were used as tools, and of skin for clothing.

Two other jet finds of that period were excavated in 1927 in the Bruder valley between Bittelbrunn and Engen. One is possibly a stylized female figure, the other a small hedgehog. All these items were drilled and possibly worn as pendants.

The rough jet is found in the southern part of the country in the region of the Swabian and Frankish alps. In the past it was excavated near Balingen, Reutlingen and Göppingen. It is also found in Würtemberg, in the form of plank jet, while cored jet is found near Tübingen.

Geologically, jet occurs in the Jurassic Poseidon layer, which corresponds to the Upper Lias of England. It was probably formed in much the same way since the Poseidon shale is also highly bituminous. Iron pyrites is frequently present and also the fossil mollusc *Posidonia bronnii*, but no ammonites are found. This suggests that the German jet may have formed in fresh water.

Jet was quite common in the Iron Age, both from the early Hallstatt period (800–400 BC) and from the later La Tène period (400–0 BC) (Rochna, 1962).The greatest concentration of finds is in the foothills of the alps just north of Lake Constance. Large quantities of lignite artifacts come also from this area and often in the form of rather thick armbands. There is more variety in the jet finds, although the jet is found in smaller quantities. Jet armbands, which are frequently found with lignite ones, are sometimes plain, occasionally flattened, ribbed or made in a triangular or hexagonal cross-section.

Large numbers of jet beads have been found, up to 200 in one necklace. From their position in relation to the skeleton on which they were found, some beads were worn as belts and some as armbands or ankle ornaments. It is common to find jet beads interspersed with bronze spirals or combined with amber, glass or clay beads or even with human teeth. A very small number of jet pins have been found consisting of a flattened sphere to which the iron pins were attached.

The source of the rough jet of this period has not been determined, but most probably it came from the Lias of the Swabian alps.

Large quantities of jet artifacts have been found in Germany on the sites of excavations of Roman towns, particularly in Cologne (Colonia Agrippinensis) and Trier (Treverorum). Most of these finds may now be seen in the Romano-Germanic Museum in Cologne. Here there are finger rings, many of which are complete, as are the large numbers of armbands. Both types may be plain or decorated. The decoration on the armbands is identical in many cases to examples found in English Roman burials (Chapter 3).

Beads are found in large quantities in the usual barrel shape or as faceted and round beads, but there are also some interesting watermelon types (*Figure 6.2*).

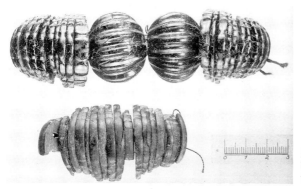

Figure 6.2 Roman segmented bracelets found in the Rhineland with two watermelon type beads

Figure 6.3 A betrothal medallion found in Germany on a string of simple circular disc beads. Compare with *Figure 3.3*

Figure 6.4 Two jet pendants with Medusa heads. Similar Roman pendants have been found in York

There are various kinds of pendants, and the interesting feature of these is how closely they match those found in York and other English sites. There are betrothal medallions showing the heads of a man and a woman (*Figure 6.3*) and others with just a lady's head. Many are decorated with the head of a Medusa (*Figure 6.4*).

Small carvings of bears are comparable to those from Malton and Colchester. A great variety of pins are found, some with very elaborately carved heads. These hair pins vary according to the hair style. Since many of these jet finds come from graves of obviously wealthy families, it is not surprising that the lady of the household would have a large selection.

Jet spindles and whorls are common and it seems that jet knife handles were popular (*Figure 6.5*). A similar jet knife handle is in the British Museum. Many of these are highly decorated and elaborately carved. The excellence of carving is also seen in small statues of boys. Perhaps the most interesting piece is a highly stylized figure of a lion (*Figure 6.6*). It is noteworthy that a broken rear half of a similar lion

Figure 6.5 Roman knife handles of jet from
the Rhineland

Figure 6.6 A Romano-German stylized lion

was found in excavations at Silchester (Lawson, 1976). All these objects have been
described in detail by Hagen (1937). The question they pose is 'where did all the jet
come from'? Were the items made in Germany or in Britain?

There is no evidence to suggest that rough jet was being excavated anywhere in
Germany in Roman times, in spite of its common use in the pre-Roman period. In
Spain at that time jet was of local importance only and Spanish jet was not exported
before the medieval period. It must be concluded therefore that the jet came from
Britain and probably from Yorkshire. Was the jet brought to Germany in its rough

state and carved there? The answer lies in the extremely close similarity between the Romano-German and Romano-British artifacts. Not only were the same types of articles made, bit the design, the carving and the decoration are in many objects all but identical. On looking at the Rhineland jet one can find, time after time, a corresponding piece in an British Roman example.

No trace of any Roman jet workshop has ever been discovered in Germany and neither have any half worked pieces ever been found. It must be concluded, therefore, that the finished articles were imported from Britain. In view of the excellent sea routes between Britain and the Rhineland in Roman times, it has been suggested that jet may have been exchanged for Romano-German glass which has been found in York. The large amounts of jet found in the Rhineland, added to those found in Roman sites all over Britain, suggest that the Roman jet industry was of not inconsiderable size.

The old German colloquial name for jet was Agstein or Augstein, and a jet turner was known as an Augsteindreher. The first historical reference to a jet

Figure 6.7 A rosary combining jet beads with silver filigree typical of the work of the medieval silversmiths of Schwäbisch Gmünd

industry in Germany refers to a quarrel between jet miners in south Germany in 1414. There is a will on record from 1431 in which a certain Dietrich Augsteindreher bequeathed a mine to his son. The trade centred on the town of Schwäbisch Gmünd and reached its peak in the 16th centry. The jet was found in the neighbourhood of the town in the Jurassic rocks, sometimes enclosed in chalk.

The industry was well organized into guilds. In the 16th century there were two guilds of jet turners and nine of jet cutters. Neither was allowed to do the work of the other. Boys had to serve a two-year apprenticeship, and the masterpiece consisted of a jet spindle and a rosary 'with good round beads', 6 oz in weight, all to be fashioned in one day in the presence of three Guildmasters.

The regulations for the guilds, laid down in 1549 for the cutters and in 1561 for the turners, can still be seen in the city archives of Schwäbisch Gmünd. There were inspectors to see that the regulations were enforced and they had to take an oath: 'You will swear that you check honestly the jet which is to be worked and see that the product which is not well done is thrown away. You will check without prejudice to anyone as has been done since ancient times'.

The jet rosaries made in Gmünd were famous and were exported to Italy, Spain, Portugal and France (*Figure 6.7*). A writer in 1596 says 'the most illustrious craftsmen were the makers of little beads made from crystal, jet, bone and wood.' Schwäbisch Gmünd was well known in medieval times for its gold and silver trades, and these continued long after the jet trade had declined. In the 15th and 16th centuries the jet trade flourished, mainly producing rosaries, crosses, pendants, buttons and beads (*Figures 6.8* and *6.9*). Unfortunately, very few examples remain today. The trade declined in the 17th century, perhaps due to the Reformation, but the gold and silver trades still continue.

It is surprising that so little is left of an industry which lasted for at least two centuries. The Schwäbisch Gmünd museum has a few exhibits of jet, but some are

Figure 6.8 A medieval cross of jet in silver. German 16th century

Figure 6.9 A Pieta of high-quality workmanship at present in the collection of the museum of Schwäbisch Gmünd, Germany. However, there is no evidence that it was locally made and it could well be of Spanish origin

Figure 6.10 One bead of a medieval rosary at present in the museum of Schwäbisch Gmünd. The pecten shells are strongly indicative of Spanish origin (see p.103)

undoubtedly of Spanish origin (*Figure 6.10*). There is one jet rosary that is combined with silver filigree work which is typical of the town (*Figure 6.7*). It appears that until recently no interest has been shown in preserving this historical aspect of the town and there is no interest at the present time in the working of jet. It is not known whether any deposits of jet still exist in Germany.

Spain

Unlike most other European names for jet, the Spanish name does not derive from the Roman gagates. In Spain jet is known as azabache. There are some regional variations in the spelling: Galician – *azebiche*, Catalan – *acebaja*, Valencian – *acabaig* and Portuguese – *azeviche*. The origin of the name is uncertain and there are many theories. One suggests that the word has an Arabic origin and means 'a stone threaded on a string' or a 'black stone'. Another suggests that it is derived from the spoken Persian. It is certain that the name was originally brought to Spain by the Moors. The word azabacheria is used to refer to the place where jet is worked and to the works themselves, and the jet worker is referred to as an azabachero. The Spanish also use the expression 'as black as jet', but for them it not only suggests the colour but also the supernatural significance of the stone.

Deposits of jet and lignite occur in many parts of Spain, but the best jet is found in Asturias. Here it was mined in Villaviciosa, Villaverde and Arguero. In the neighbourhood of Oviedo a dark compact lignite is found and a small industry grew up in this region using the local product. Lignite was also found in Santander. Poorer quality jet came from Teruel and from Portugal.

In the 19th century, at the height of the Whitby jet industry, much jet was imported into England from Spain, but it was found to be of poor quality or even soft jet. Thus in Whitby, Spanish jet acquired a bad reputation. Perhaps there was a certain amount of patriotic prejudice involved, for in Spain the jet workers condemned jet imported from France and Portugal for its poor quality and called it the 'false stone'.

Tests done on a few samples of Spanish jet (Muller, 1980) have shown a high proportion of sulphur (see *Figure 1.2b*), and this confirmed an observation made in 1874 (Anon) which, describing the tendency of ornaments made from Spanish jet to break up under the influence of sudden heat or cold, says 'this fragility is believed to be due to a small percentage of sulphur which most Spanish jet contains'. In spite of the unfavourable views held by the Whitby jet workers, there is no doubt that the hard Spanish jet is of as good a quality as may be found anywhere.

The history of the Spanish jet industry is closely tied to the history of the Galician town of Santiago de Compostela (*Figure 6.11*). Like Whitby, this is a very picturesque town retaining a medieval atmosphere in its narrow streets and beautifully preserved old buildings. The name can be translated as St. James of the Field of Stars (campus stellae) and the entire town grew as a shrine to Saint James, the patron Saint of all Spain.

In the year 44 AD St. James the Elder was beheaded in Jerusalem, but it was believed that his embalmed remains were brought to Spain and buried there.

Figure 6.11 Santiago de Compostela in Northern Spain, the centre of the Spanish jet industry

Figure 6.12 Statues of St. James the Great over the 'Holy Door' leading into the cathedral from the Quintana de Los Muertos

Almost 800 years later, in 813, his tomb was rediscovered and on its site a church and a monastery were built. These were the foundations of the town which was to undergo varied fortunes over the next 200 years, being sacked by the Vikings in the 9th century and by the Moors in the 10th.

The present cathedral dates back to the 10th century and presents a mixture of styles from the magnificent Romanesque Portico de la Gloria carved in the 12th century to the Baroque facade which was finished in the 18th. The cathedral dominates the town (*Figure 6.11*) and is surrounded by the well preserved old part while the new town is kept firmly on the outskirts.

The shrine of St. James soon became an important centre of pilgrimage, ranking in stature with Rome and Jerusalem. In 1181 a Papal Bull granted remission of their sins to those who completed the pilgrimage, particularly in a Holy Year when the Saint's day, July 25th, falls on a Sunday. In the last Holy Year, 1965, over two

Figure 6.13 The pilgrim hat of Stephan Praun 1544–91, worn on his journeys of pilgrimage to Santiago de Compostela and Jerusalem. The hat is decorated with souvenirs in jet, ivory and pecten shells. Between the shells is a small statue of St. James and on top of the hat a jet plaque showing St. James on horseback

million pilgrims visited the town, not perhaps travelling on foot on the old pilgrim's way but more comfortably and swiftly by Iberian Airlines.

In medieval times a pilgrim was given a souvenir as a certificate of his journey (*Figure 6.13*). These usually took the form of a cap badge and were made of lead or brass, but in Santiago de Compostela they were carved of jet. Perhaps because of its proximity to the sea, the symbol of St. James was the scallop shell which is also the sign of a pilgrim and a symbol of eternity. The making of these shells for pilgrims was the origin of the jet industry which started in the 13th century, rose to its height in the 15th and declined by the end of the 17th century.

The industry was very involved with pilgrimage and the church and, as might be expected, most of its products were of a religious nature. As well as the shells, the jet workers produced small sculptures of the Holy Family, of the Virgin and Child, and pietas, crucifixes, rosaries, rings and crosses (*Figures 6.14, 6.15* and *6.16*). But by far the most popular carvings were small statuettes of St. James (*Figure 6.17*). In these the Saint is dressed as a pilgrim with an upturned hat in which there is a shell. He usually carries a staff, a bible and a drinking gourd. Sometimes he is accompanied by kneeling pilgrims in miniature. Rich patrons may have especially ordered statuettes with their own likeness carved into these small pilgrim figures.

All the early representations of St. James were of this type. In the 17th century, however, he was depicted as a warrior on horse back, the Matamoros, the killer of Moors. Only about five of these equestrian statuettes are still extant. At the time they were regarded as a protection against robbers. Examples of small statues of St. James can now be found in museums all over Europe and in America. They give evidence of their widespread journeying as well as of the hard quality of the jet which has endured for centuries. The best collection of these medieval carvings is in the Instituto de Valencia de Don Juan in Madrid. A good collection is also in the museum of Pontevedra, and in America one is owned by the Hispanic Society of New York.

Figure 6.14 A jet crucifix of the late 16th century. Size 240 × 380 mm

Figure 6.15 A portapaz in jet showing St. James with two kneeling pilgrims. Early 16th century. (A portapaz is given to believers to kiss during mass and wish for peace)

Figure 6.16 A jewellery box made of carved jet. Early 17th century

Figure 6.17 Jet statuette of St. James from the 16th century. Height 150 mm

As in the German medieval industry, the jet workers of Santiago were also organized into guilds. The Brotherhood of Jet Workers was established in 1443, about 100 years earlier than their German counterpart. In Santiago there was a separate Chapter of the Shell Workers. The rules of the guild were strict. The first rule was that only true jet which 'takes the straw' should be used, and false jet which would not stand up to sun, air and heat should never be used. This shows that they were well aware of the differences between soft and hard jet and of its electrical property. Other rules stated that jet products should only be sold in the Azabacheria in Santiago and should never be sold privately (from the house) or in the inns. They were prohibited from repairing jet by gluing pieces together 'except for the turned feet of the crosses'.

Gilding and silvering were not allowed in case they were used to disguise cracks in the jet. Strict rules were also laid down for the behaviour of apprentices and masters and for the religious responsibilities of all the members of the guild. Once a year a mass was held where every jet worker had to be present and bring with him a thick wax candle. Jet workers from outside the town, who wished to sell their wares in Santiago, had to present themselves within three days to the Elders of the Guild. During that time the local members could buy their goods at cost price. Only after that were the outsiders allowed to sell in Santiago and then only if their goods came up to the required standard and at a price fixed by the guild. Failure to conform to this procedure meant that all their work could be confiscated without compensation.

All this was designed to protect the workers of Santiago from competition with the people living in the valleys of Asturias. However, by the beginning of the 16th century such strict controls were abandoned because the local jet workers could not produce sufficient to meet the huge demand of the pilgrims. They had to rely on supplies from these provincial workshops to augment their own products.

As the 16th century progressed and the trade continued to expand the quality of the work suffered, giving way to quantity, so that at the end of the century the industry started to decline. The number of pilgrims also decreased so that the workers had to turn to objects of a non-religious nature to keep the trade going. Black chains and earrings became fashionable as mourning jewellery, especially for widows. In the 17th century the guild survived by the production of secular jewellery and particularly by the production of the higa (*Figure 6.18*).

The higa, or 'phallic hand', is an amulet whose use and importance stretches from the 10th century to the present day. The hand has had a magical significance since early Egyptian times and can be found as Egyptian, Phoenician and Roman amulets. The higa was brought to Spain by the Moors in the 10th century. It consists of a hand with the thumb protruding between the first and second finger. This was worn as a protection against the evil eye. Apparently extending one's hand in this aggressive gesture was supposed to shock the evil one so much that he would run away. However that may be, the higa has been regarded as a protection against evil and illness for many centuries.

While jet was regarded as a talisman, even if worn as an unpolished piece, when carved into a higa the magical powers of the two combined to produce a powerful charm. The concept of the higa, or closed hand, is basically opposed to that of the shell or open hand. While the shell was held to be a sacred object, the higa was

Figure 6.18 Two higas, the left with a silver mount. Each has a cross within a circle combining the Christian symbol with the supernatural force of the higa

Figure 6.19 The Infante Don Felipe Prosper, painted in 1659 by Diego Rodrigues de Silva y Velasquez. Note the jet higa on the left shoulder, also a bell, horn and pomander hung from the waist

based on superstition and the power of the supernatural. In 1525 Charles V unsuccessfully attempted to prohibit the wearing of jet higas because they were un-Christian. He did not object to the jet itself, but only to the hand. Nevertheless the higa continued to be used, particularly by parents, who would pin a small one on to a child's dress to protect him from illness (*Figure 6.19*).

In the Middle Ages many elaborate and highly decorated higas were produced and may still be seen in museum collections. Some were incised with the Christian cross, a potent combination of supernatural and religious beliefs. Later the higa assumed a more natural appearance, and it is still being made today in all sizes.

At the end of the 17th century there was a decline in the number of pilgrims and, perhaps because of the religious wars, the jet trade decreased drastically. The last records of the Brotherhood of jet workers are for 1747. In 1752 only four jet workers are named in the trade register of the town. With the death of the industry all interest in it was lost until the 19th century. It is due to the endeavours of two or three men that the history of this old trade is now preserved and documented so well. The Count of Valencia collected medieval jet objects and his extensive collection is now preserved in the museum which bears his name in Madrid. The documentation of the industry is due to a lawyer who lived in Santiago at the end of the 19th century and whose interest was a study of the old legal documents of the town. It is thanks to Senor Lopez Ferriero that so much is known about the old guilds and about conditions of work, rates of pay and the names of the old masters.

There is a strong similarity between England and Spain in the way in which jet has come into and gone out of fashion over the centuries. Yet the Whitby industry, which is only about 100 years old, has never been as well studied or documented as the much older Spanish industry.

The renaissance of the Spanish jet industry in the present century has been attributed to Enrique Mayer (1861–1931). Of German descent, he came to Santiago de Compostela at the end of the 19th century and began again the lost art of carving in jet. He passed his talents on to his son and to his great nephew, Fernando Mayer, who is the present representative of the family. The Mayer family have a small but prestigious shop set into the wall of the cathedral in the Plaza de Las Platerias right next to the steps of the cathedral (*Figure 6.20*). Apart from the Mayer family there are in Santiago today at least three other fully trained craftsmen whose work is of the highest standard. On visiting one of these men, Ramon Requeixo Rebon, in his workshop, the first impression is that of a spotlessly white walled room. What a contrast to the old jet workshops of Whitby which were black with dust and debris (*Figure 6.21*). Ramon learnt the art of carving at night school and spent five years learning to be a master craftsman. His work is of a standard to equal if not to surpass that of many of the 19th century Whitby workers. As might be expected, his best figures are all religious. So too is the work of Ramon Gonzalez Taboada (*Figure 6.22*). Both men produce figures of St. James; the former prefers the traditional pilgrim figure, the latter has his own artistic interpretation of the Saint (*Figure 6.23*). The statuettes take from two to three months to complete and sell for between £200 and £500 each. Obviously they are not made in large numbers. Both shops had five or six of these top-quality carvings for sale.

Figure 6.20 The Mayer shop in Santiago de Compostela

Figure 6.21 The workshop of Ramon Rebon. Notice the raw jet, hand tools and a small statue in the process of being made

Figure 6.22 Ramon Gonzales Taboada, one of the four master craftsmen working in Santiago today

The present teacher of jet carving at the night school is Ricardo Rivas Mejuto, who is a qualified art teacher and specializes in sculpture. All four of these master craftsmen regard themselves as sculptors and work in ivory as well as jet. In some cases the two materials are combined in unusual ways. For example a group of Mary, Joseph and the baby Jesus is made in jet with faces and hands of ivory. The baby Jesus is also beautifully carved in ivory.

As many of these carvings are up to 250 mm in height and executed in the round, it is evident that quite large pieces of good-quality jet are required. The rough jet still comes from Villaviciosa in Asturias, where there is only one man, Thomas Noval, who still mines it and that only sporadically, so that the top-quality jet is always in short supply. The mine has been owned for the past 30 years by English people who apparently are not interested in the jet. The seams of jet are wide in comparison to those normally found around Whitby. Some seams are over 50 mm thick with little or no flaws. No doubt the availability of such seams limits the

Figure 6.23 A modern statue of St. James by
Ramon Taboada. Height, 180 mm (shown
approximately actual size)

making of the statuettes and naturally the present-day jet workers have a wide range of other, smaller, products.

Next in complexity of workmanship are the cameos. These are again often of Saint James or other religious figures, but some are of young girls. Here the workmanship is not equal to the best of the 19th century cameo carvers of Whitby. The cameos are made in much lower relief, more like a shell cameo and none are of the quality of a Speedy or Greenbury. Other ornaments are higas of sizes ranging from 20 mm to 50 mm in length, small animals and faceted beads. Usually the beads have less facets than the best of Victorian Whitby beads, but because they are time-consuming to make they are costly, a 500 mm necklace being priced at £195.

The master craftsmen are also trained silversmiths and mount their cameos and higas in silver. Cameos are never mounted in a jet surround as in Whitby. Apart from these four masters, there are many men who are not so highly trained but who also work with jet. These men usually do it as a hobby in their own homes producing small polished cabochons for setting into pre-made silver mounts. This type of jewellery for the tourist trade is on sale in many shops in Santiago. It includes bracelets, earrings, pendants and so on. All consist of a cabochon of jet mounted in a precast silver setting of a design characteristic of this region of Spain. This type of jewellery is less expensive and ranges in price from about £6 for a simple silver ring set with a small jet cabochon to about £30 for a similar brooch and upwards for more elaborate designs.

When reviewing the articles made today in the Spanish jet industry one is aware of the very wide gap between the wonderful carved statues and the cheap tourist souvenirs. The area in between is very lacking in quantity when compared with the wide range of jewellery and ornaments made by the Whitby jet workers of the 19th century. Although there are bracelets and earrings of silver and jet there is no evidence that anyone makes bracelets entirely of jet, or earrings of the wonderful complexity of design which can be found in the Victorian jewellery.

One of the criticisms of the Whitby jet industry was that it became tradition bound and lacking in new ideas. Perhaps this is a common fault, for it appears that the jet workers of Santiago de Compostela are also set in their ways, repeating old designs and not trying anything new. Yet their skill is undeniable.

The method of working the jet is basically very similar to that used in Whitby in the last century. The jet is chopped out and roughly shaped with a chisel or saw. All the carving is done by hand with a wide variety of tools, many of which are home-made. The lathe is no longer turned by treadle and fly wheel but is electrically operated. It is used for turning beads against a carborundum wheel and also holds various brushes for the polishing process. Hand polishing is done as it is here, with sand paper, 'wet and dry' and finally Brasso. Beads are usually drilled with a simple hand-held bow drill.

Today, Spain is the only country in the world, other than England, where there is a living jet industry. What of the future? Supplies of good-quality jet are available in both countries. Most important is the fact that in Spain jet carving is being taught in the College of Further Education and young men are learning the craft from the masters. This will ensure that the art is not lost, as it almost has been in Whitby. If there is ever to be a revival of an industry in Whitby on the scale of that which existed in the last century, there must be someone like Enrique Mayer with the knowledge and the desire to revive the ancient art of jet carving and to teach it to the young artists.

Finally, mention must be made of the so-called 'azabache compacto' which is to be found on sale in some of the tourist shops in Santiago. This material is made into a variety of good luck charms. It is said to be jet dust mixed with some undisclosed substance in a 'secret process'. Certainly the material is a very effective imitation of jet. It is interesting to recall that, in Whitby during the height of the industry, many attempts were made to find a use for the copious supply of jet dust, but none were found. The product on sale in Spain is quite hard and takes a good polish. It could possibly be a mixture of jet dust with an epoxy resin.

France

In France jet is known today as jais, jaiet or jayet, and in the past has been called gest or getz. It was known in prehistoric times although not many relics have been found. A Neolithic burial find in Couriac, Department Aveyron, produced a necklace of jet and chalk together with other chalk jewellery (*Figure 6.24*).

Jet appears to have been a popular decorative material in France in the Middle Ages. A '*History of Furniture*' (Havard, 1887) gives some examples from the 13th century onwards including:

1228   In the inventory of Clemencia of Hungary, a widow of Louis X of France, a jet rosary.

Figure 6.24 A neolithic necklace of jet and chalk found in France

1380   In the inventory of Charles V, six pieces of jet (gest).
1524   A mirror in black jet (gaie) in the shape of a heart, and a robe of black satin embroidered with jet (getz).
1589   In the inventory of Catherine de Médicis, four chandeliers of jet (getz).
1598   A mirror decorated with jet (jayet).

The words in brackets give the French word used.

Jet was frequently combined with rock crystal, amber and ivory, and as early as the 17th century was imitated using black glass. It was customary in France to have mourning furniture in black, and in 1680 in the inventory of Henry of Béthune a font of jet is mentioned.

The rough jet was found in the greensand of the Cretaceous formation in the Department Aude, province of Languedoc. It occurred in thin seams, similar to the plank jet of Yorkshire. It was mined at Monjardin near Chalabre, on Mount Commo-Escuro and on Mount Cerbeiron. It was also found in Roquevaire near Marseilles and Belestat in the Pyrenees.

The French jet working industry was at its height in the 18th century. Bauer (1904) says that in 1786 there were 1200 people employed in it. It was centred on Sainte Colombe and Labastide-sur-l'Hers. Some of the finished products were exported to Spain, Italy, Germany and Turkey. The French were particularly well known for their rosaries, but by the early 19th century the industry had declined to a small fraction of its former production. Whether the supply of jet ran out is not known, but even in its heyday some rough jet was imported from Spain. Certainly by the 19th century, when the Whitby industry was at its height and supplies of local jet were running low, an attempt was made to import rough jet from France. What happened is described in an article in the *Whitby Gazette* of 1871:

'An enterprising local speculator attempted to import cheap jet from France. It was a signal and hopeless failure. The jet, if it may be dignified by that name, was so inferior to local jet that it was quite useless for manufacture. It was brittle, soft and crumbly and could easily be broken. None was sold.'

It is interesting to note that the 19th century *History of Furniture*, quoted above, says that jet is found in France, Spain and Germany, whereas English jet is not mentioned. At about the same time a Larousse encyclopaedia also gives the same sources and again does not mention English jet.

By the end of the 19th century all manufacture of jet had ended in France. No doubt the use of black glass, the so called French jet, had completely replaced the use of the original natural material.

The United States of America

Jet occurs in Colorado, New Mexico, Utah and North Dakota, the principal sources being Utah and Colorado. In Utah the jet is found in coal seams. In a desert county south of Hanksville on the north slopes of Mount Ellen is an area known as Coaly Basin. Jet from here was mined and marketed in the early part of the 20th century. Reports say that it was good hard jet.

In Colorado there are records of large amounts of jet coming from El Paso County. The area mined was south of Colorado Springs and is now the US Army's Fort Carson Military Reservation. From 1926 to 1930 jet was produced commercially from this region and some specimens may be seen in the H. E. Mather collection in Colorado College, Colorado Springs.

Compared with England, very little jet was utilized in the USA for the manufacture of jewellery, except by the American Indians who used it for their mosaic and inlay work. The Pueblo Indians ranked it second only to turquoise and successfully combined the two in their jewellery. Jet was often inlaid with turquoise in the making of pendants, rings and amulets. In 1896 a jet frog was found in excavations of a burial in Pueblo Bonito, New Mexico (Kunz, 1913). It had turquoise eyes and a turquoise band around its neck. Frogs were a favourite theme for amulets and small jet frogs have been found in many Indian burials. It is possible that the finding of a frog in the desert would indicate the presence of water (*Figure 6.25*).

Figure 6.25 A jet frog with turquoise eyes on a necklace of jet and turquoise made by the Pueblo Indians

The Indians loved fine jewellery, esteemed it as wealth, and wore it profusely. Jet is said to represent to the Pueblo Indians the sacred black colour of the nadir, one of their six directions (King, 1976). They often referred to it as black turquoise.

The Anasazi tribe utilized jet in their jewellery before the Spanish conquest to make disc-shaped beads. The jet was ground to the right thickness with sandstone then scored and broken into squares. The rough disc was formed by breaking the edges, then it was drilled with a stone-tipped bow drill or cactus spine. The discs were then strung together tightly and ground on a sandstone slab until of uniform roundness. This method probably compares with the method used by the Bronze Age bead makers in England.

At the present time, the Zuni indians make very colourful jewellery of silver inlaid with turquoise and jet. Although local jet is available, it tends to crack easily and it is reported that they prefer to use Whitby jet when they can get it (*Figure 6.26* and colour plate).

Figure 6.26 A Zuni Indian drilling a piece of turquoise with a hand-held bow drill

References

Germany

ADAM, K. D. 'Eiszeitkunst in Süddeutschland', *Kosmos*, **8**, (1978)

DANGEL, A., *Vom ehemaligen Gmünder Gagatbergbau*, Gmünder Heimatblätter (1960)

FREH, W., 'Alte Gagatbergbaue in den nördlichen Ostalpen', *Joanneum Mineralogisches Mitteilungsblatt* (1955)

HAGEN, W., 'Kaiserzeitliche Gagatarbeiten aus dem Rheinischen Germanien', *Bonner Jahrbücher des Rheinischen Landesmuseums in Bonn*, **142,** Darmstadt (1937)

KLEIN, W., 'Das Gewerbe der Augsteindreher und Schneider', *Geschichte des Gmünder Goldschmiedegewerbes*, Stuttgart (1920)

LAWSON, A. J. 'Shale and jet objects from Silchester', *Archaeologia*, 241 (1976)

ROCHNA, O., 'Hallstattzeitlicher Lignit- und Gagat-Schmuck. Zur Verbreitung, Zeitstellung und Herkunft,' *Fundberichte aus Schwaben*, Vol. 16 (1962)

Spain

ANON, *All the year round* (1874)

ANON, *Objects in the collection of the Hispanic Society of America* (1930)

CALDERÓN, *Los Minerales de Espana* (1910)

COX, I. (ed.), *The Scallop: Studies of a shell and its influence on human kind*, Shell Transports Ltd. (1957)

FERRANDIS, J., *Marfiles y azabaches Espanoles*, Editorial Labor, Barcelona (1938)

FILGUEIRA VALVERDE, J., 'Azabacheria', *Cuadernos de Arte Gallego*, 17, Vigo

FORTNUM, C. D. E. 'Notes on other Signacula of St. James of Compostela', *The Archaeological Journal*, Vol. 38 (1881)

GOMEZ-TABANERA, 'Azabache Amuleto de la vieja Europa y ambar negro de Asturias', *Oviedo Boletin del Instituto de Estudios Asturianos* (1978)

VAN LOO, E., 'Les Jais ou azabaches de Compostela', *Les Jardin des Arts* (October, 1955)

LÓPEZ FERREIRO, A., *Historia de la Santa A. M. Inglesia de Santiago de Compostela*, Vol. 5, Santiago (1898–1902)

DE OSMA Y SCULL, G., *Catálogo de Azabaches Compostelanos*, Madrid (1916)

VAUGHAN, M., 'Rare old Spanish carvings in jet', *International Studio,* Vol. 84, June (1926)

WILLIAMS, L., *The arts and crafts of older Spain,* Vol. 3, Chicago (1908)

France

BAUER, M., *Precious Stones,* Charles Griffin and Co., London (1904)

EBERT, M., *Real-Lexikon der Vorgeschichte,* Vol. 4, Berlin (1926)

HAVARD, H., *Dictionnaire de l'Ameublement,* 4 Vols., May and Motteroz, Paris (1887)

The United States of America

JACKA, J. D. and HAMMACK, N. S., *Indian Jewellery of the prehistoric southwest,* The University of Arizona Press, Tucson (1975)

JERNIGAN, E. W., *Jewellery in the prehistoric southwest,* University of New Mexico Press, Albuquerque (1978)

KING, D. S., *Indian silver,* Vol. 2, Tucson (1976)

KUNZ, G. F., *The curious lore of precious stones,* Halcyon House, New York (1913)

Chapter 7
Simulants

There is more difference between thy flesh and
hers, than between jet and ivory.

Shakespeare

Introduction

With its aura of magic and its reputation as a talisman, jet was already a valuable
jewel in ancient times. Even very early Stone Age artifacts from south Germany
show that jet was being imitated by less valuable materials, although deliberate
imitation would be hard to prove. Many natural materials made into jewellery and
similar to jet in appearance are found dating from the Bronze Age. They include
lignite and shale. Later cannel coal, anthracite and Kimmeridge shale were in use.

During jet's immensely popular period in the 19th century bog oak and horn
were employed as substitutes. Black onyx and chalcedony can also be included in
this section, although they were jewels in their own right and only incidentally
resemble jet because of their colour.

Far more important commercially were the man-made simulants which appeared
as early as 1845 in the form of vulcanite and black glass. Other materials of similar
appearance in use in the 19th century were gutta percha and bois durci, but few of
these are found today.

Finally the 20th century brought into use bakelite and other plastics including,
more recently, epoxy resin.

Kimmeridge shale

A naturally occurring substance which is found in England and which can closely
resemble jet is Kimmeridge shale. Many grave objects in this material were found
during the 19th century excavations and are still often labelled as jet. It would be
incorrect to say that articles of Kimmeridge shale were made with the intention of
imitating jet jewellery. Its manufacture was an independent industry which
flourished for 800 years.

Kimmeridge shale is a highly bituminous shale containing marine fossils, which
forms part of the Kimmeridge clay formation in the Isle of Purbeck in Dorset in the
south of England. When freshly quarried it has the appearance of slate. It is light in
weight (its specific gravity is 1.285) and of grey-black to brownish-black colour.
Like jet it shows a conchoidal fracture. When first quarried it is dull, but when

smoothed and polished with beeswax, it looks remarkably like jet. Unlike jet, however, it does not retain its lustre over the centuries and artifacts of Kimmeridge shale when excavated are invariably cracked or broken into small pieces. This deterioration is thought to be due to the loss of oil through evaporation or chemical change.

Nevertheless as many articles of Kimmeridge shale as of jet are found from excavations during the period when it was in use. This extended from the Iron Age to the end of the Roman occupation of Britain; that is roughly from the 4th century BC to the 4th century AD. It reached its height in Roman times after the introduction of the lathe in the 1st century AD. See *Figure 7.1*.

The shale was quarried from the cliffs east and west of Kimmeridge. It was taken to neighbouring occupation sites to be worked. The principal product appears to have been armlets. Judging by the waste shale found in the area, there must have been a sizeable production of these ornaments. The waste shale is found as flat circular discs and when first discovered was thought to be 'coal money'. However, further research showed the true nature of the discs and how the armlets were made.

The shale was first broken into slabs 12–18 mm thick and then a circle 75 mm in diameter was marked out with a compass. A hole was pecked out of one side to fit

Figure 7.1 Romano-British table-leg made of Kimmeridge Shale, found in the Colliton Park excavation in Dorchester (approximate height, 900 mm)

the disc onto a lathe. The edge was then worked smooth using a flint chisel. The centre of the disc was then cut out and a ring was obtained. The central core could sometimes be used for a second smaller ring before being discarded (Calkin, 1953).

These armlets were at first rather thick and plain, but in the Roman period they were finer and were often decorated. The decorations of beading or notching around the edge can also be seen in jet arm bands of the same period. Although armlets are the most common form of jewellery made from Kimmeridge shale, a few pendants have also been found. Often identified in the original report as jet, the cracked and broken appearance suggests their more likely source. Kimmeridge shale artifacts were mostly distributed in the south of England although a few were found in Roman towns further north, such as Lincoln and York (Cunliffe, 1974).

Lignite

Lignite is a term covering a group of coal-like deposits intermediate between peat and bituminous coal. Under the microscope it shows that the original plant cell structure is less compacted and distorted than in jet. Unlike Kimmeridge shale there was no centre for the production of lignite jewellery, yet its use was widespread in ancient times.

In Germany in the Celtic period the use of lignite preceded that of jet. In Britain in Roman sites articles of lignite are found together with Kimmeridge shale and jet.

Lignite is brownish in colour and lacks the lustre and deep black colour of jet. It does not survive the centuries without cracking and breaking up. At best it could only be poor imitation, possibly a substitute when jet was not available. Although it was more readily found than jet, its use was limited to antiquity and none was used after Roman times.

Anthracite

Anthracite is a compact, dense, brittle substance whose colour is as black as jet. However, it has a glassy or metallic lustre, a 'harder' look than the soft lustre of jet. It has an uneven or conchoidal fracture and a hardness of 2. It consists of 99% carbon and burns with a blue flame and much less smoke than jet. It is found in Wales, Pennsylvania, China, the USSR and South Africa, and in small coalfields in other locations.

In Britain small ornaments have been made from it. The most commonly found items today are small bibles,often crudely executed. They were probably made as a hobby by the miners. In some coalfields quite elaborate structures, such as a full-size archway, have been built as advertisements for the coal companies.

In the USA anthracite is found in many places in eastern Pennsylvania and in the past was used extensively for ornaments. Although not as tough as jet it takes a brilliant polish and is sufficiently resistant to abrasion as not to rub off on fingers or clothing.

Figure 7.2 The coal house built in 1940 from 40 tons of coal for the Middlesboro, Kentucky, Chamber of Commerce

Coal carving was carried out in America in Victorian times at such places as Mounting Top near Glen Summit, at the Franklin mine in Ashley, the Spring Tunnel mine, the Summit mine and Nanticoke. It was carved into boots, anchors, hearts, vases, paperweights and so on. Kunz (1890) says that the best work was done by a one-armed man at Glen Summit. Many coal yards had impressive monuments of anthracite outside their offices showing the name of the colliery and the company similar to those which can still be seen in South Wales. In Middlesboro, Kentucky, in 1940, an entire house was built from 40 tons of coal (*Figure 7.2*). There is no record of anthracite carving being carried out on any scale at the present time.

Cannel coal

Sometimes called 'candle coal', cannel coal is a sapropelic coal composed largely of finely disintegrated plant debris. It was formed in stagnant water and is rich in spores, resin bodies and leaf cuticle. All of these can be seen in thin section under the microscope. The colour is not as black as jet and in certain directions the broken surface has a silvery grey sheen. It does not take such a high polish as jet, but when polished the colour darkens and it can be mistaken for jet. The black powder produced by scratching the material and a black streak left on unglazed porcelain are diagnostic. Like jet, cannel coal shows a conchoidal fracture but the fracture's surface will often show its true nature by being dull and greyish in colour in contrast to the lustrous black of the fracture of jet.

Cannel coal has more volatile hydrocarbons than jet and fragments burn more easily with more flame and less smoke. It is found in large masses in the coal measures of Newcastle and in Scotland. Large pieces are therefore available for carving and it has been used not only for ornaments but also for the veneer of furniture. In Scotland in the 19th century, there was a small industry making snuff boxes, miniature tables and shoes and other souvenirs. Jewellery was seldom made. In the late 18th and early 19th centuries a certain Robert Town of Wigan was renowned for his figures carved from cannel coal and some examples of his work are to be seen in the British Museum. In Whitby, the 19th century jet workers sometimes used cannel coal for larger sculptures (*Figure 7.3*).

Figure 7.3 A plaque bearing cameos of King Oswy and his Queen carved from cannel coal. Size, 100 × 125 mm

Horn

Horn is light in weight, tough and easily worked. It is thermoplastic and can be moulded when heated in water. When stained black it makes a passable imitation of jet. In the 19th century jewellery was made of horn, mainly in the form of pendants and brooches. These articles are often rough and scaly on the reverse side and, when held up to the light, the edges may be translucent due to incomplete staining. They were sometimes inlaid with mother-of-pearl (*Figure 7.4*).

Figure 7.4 A selection of horn jewellery. Width of butterfly brooch, 50 mm

Horn does not have the deep glossy black colour of jet, but often resembles vulcanite (see below) in its appearance. When scratched it gives a grey powder and a grey streak on porcelain. These are characteristic. When a hot needle is applied to horn, a typical smell of burning hair is given off.

Bog oak

The Victorians were especially fond of anything Scottish or Irish and the native jewellery of this period was very popular. Bog oak is a black, hard, semi-fossilized wood dug out of the peat bogs of Ireland. The best suited for carving comes from the counties of Meath, Tipperary, Kerry and Donegal. It has been used for carving for centuries, but the industry making tourist souvenirs is said to have started when George IV visited Ireland in 1821 and was presented with an elaborately carved walking stick.

In 1882 there were 200 people employed in the industry, and, as in Whitby, some worked in large manufacturing premises while others worked at home. Most of the jewellery and ornaments made were typically Irish in design and decoration. They

Figure 7.5 An assortment of bog-oak ornaments. Size of harp, 85 × 153 mm

Figure 7.6 This bog-oak name brooch is very similar in appearance to one made of jet. However, the shamrocks give the clue to its origin

took the form of copies of antique brooches, such as the famous Tara brooch, Celtic crosses and brooches decorated with towers, abbeys, harps and shamrocks (*Figures 7.5* and *7.6*). Mucross Abbey near Killarney is a common decoration since Killarney was such a popular tourist attraction.

Bog oak is a very dark brown in colour, but does not take a high polish. Its matt surface is characteristic but it can resemble unpolished jet. It has no conchoidal fracture and is less brittle and more durable than jet.

Although all the early Victorian pieces were hand carved, in the late 1860s a method of stamping the design in the wood was devised. This permitted the production of much more highly decorated pieces at less expense. The piece of wood was placed on the top of the die which was then heated by means of a hot plate of metal on which it stood. Over the wood a similar hot plate was placed and screwed down. The bitumen in the wood was said to prevent the fibre from cracking (Spons, 1882).

In 1882 there were about four dealers in Dublin who specialized in bog oak trinkets and jewellery and their annual turnover was £5000. A small amount of jewellery and souvenirs is still being made today.

'French jet' (black glass)

Although a certain amount of jet was found in France (Chapter 6), its use was mainly restricted to the Middle Ages. After jet was exhibited at the Great Exhibition of 1851, it became very popular in Europe. Queen Victoria presented the Empress Eugenie of France with a pair of jet bracelets, and some jet jewellery was exported to the continent. The fashion for black jewellery in France could not be met by their own limited supplies of jet, so they began to make jewellery from black glass. It was cheaper than jet and did not need to be hand carved since glass could easily be moulded. 'French jet', as it was called, became very popular, not only for cheap jewellery but also, in particular, for decorating clothes.

Black glass jewellery was also made in England, but in smaller quantities. It was known as Vauxhall glass. Because it was coloured with manganese oxide, it has a slightly reddish or purplish tinge when held up to the light. As it was extremely brittle, especially in thin pieces, it was often mounted on Japanned black metal frames, as was much of the 'French jet'. This is seen in particular in the elaborate hair combs which were worn in the late 19th century.

The use of 'French jet' was restricted to jewellery and accessories and clothing decoration (*Figures 7.7* and *7.8*). It did not lend itself to the making of small

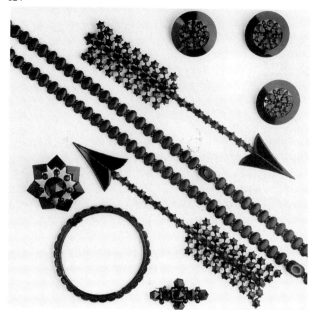

Figure 7.7 French jet ornaments, including a muff chain of 'crepe stones'. Length of arrows, 167 mm

Figure 7.8 A demi-parure of French jet. Length of necklace, 405 mm, diameter of centre star pendant, 48 mm

ornaments. Nevertheless much else which could be made in jet was copied in glass and once a mould had been made the article could be reproduced by the thousand, in a shorter time and at much less cost than jet. It was obviously serious competition for the Whitby jet trade.

Black glass beads are commonly faceted. Large beads were heavy to wear, and so hollow glass beads, painted black on the inside, were made as an experiment. They were not a success, being far too fragile to stand up to normal wear. As a result 'French jet' beads are usually small to medium in size and are never made in the really large sizes found in jet.

There is no difficulty in distinguishing black glass from jet. It is heavier, cold to the touch and brittle. It is harder than jet (about 6 on Mohs' scale) and cannot be scratched with a pin. It leaves no mark on porcelain and a heated needle does not affect it.

One type of 'French jet' which gives rise to some difficulty of identification is the 'crepe stone'. When the Victorians were in the deepest first stage of mourning they were not supposed to wear any shiny jewellery even if it was black (see Chapter 4). Jet, of course, could be left unpolished and bog oak qualified because of its lack of natural shine. But glass or 'French jet' had a particularly brilliant lustre. To counteract this the beads were sometimes treated to give a 'bloomed' finish. These were called crepe stones because they resembled the dull crepe material which was obligatory for mourning dress. These dull glass beads are frequently found nowadays in the form of muff chains. They are usually flattened in the form of small hearts or bean shaped. They are usually double threaded and interspersed with tiny round glass beads (*Figure 7.7*).

When selling 'French jet' jewellery in the UK it is advisable to add the description (black glass) since the term 'French jet' does not comply with the Trade Descriptions Act. The article is neither jet nor necessarily French, since black glass jewellery was, and still is, made in England.

Vulcanite

In 1846 Charles Goodyear patented a process in America which consisted of mixing rubber with 30% sulphur and then heating it to 115°C. The result was a hard material called vulcanite or ebonite. In 1856 Thomas Hancock patented a similar process in England. Goodyear was mainly interested in making rubber tyres, but his product turned out to be the most successful simulant of jet. When new it was light in weight, black in colour and could be polished until its lustre was very nearly as good as that of jet. Most significantly, it could be moulded on moderate heating. Thus, as with glass, once a mould had been cast, many thousands of pieces of jewellery could be produced quickly and cheaply. The objects which were most successful in vulcanite were brooches, pendants and chains. Like glass it was seldom used for ornaments, but unlike glass it does not appear to have been used for dress decoration. Vulcanite beads were also not very impressive.

Vulcanite soon became a most successful competitor for jet, and it is interesting today to find examples of the same design executed in both vulcanite and jet. Its light weight and excellent black colour were probably as misleading to the

Victorians as they still are to many antique dealers today. Stories are still told in Whitby of how the more unscrupulous manufacturers or their agents would come to Whitby and buy one or two excellent carved brooches or pendants and within weeks flood the market with cheap copies.

It was difficult for the Whitby jet trade to compete with this man-made product. As there was no Trade Description Act in the 19th century one wonders how many Victorian ladies who thought they were wearing jet were in fact wearing vulcanite. At the present time many people declare quite vehemently that a certain black necklace must be jet because 'it belonged to my great grandmother', when it is in fact black glass or vulcanite. It is strange how we think of plastics as being a 20th-century invention.

According to *Kelly's Directory* there were 16 manufacturers of vulcanite in the UK in 1880. Although, when new, vulcanite was very similar in appearance to jet, it had the great disadvantage of losing its colour if exposed to sunlight. As a result of oxidation it would change from black through brown to khaki and then a dirty yellow. However, if protected from the sun, the colour remains as good today as it was 100 years ago.

Like jet, vulcanite produces a brown powder when scratched and a brown streak on porcelain. It is the only imitation of jet to do this and is thus the most difficult to identify. It is said that when rubbed, the smell of sulphur is noticeable. One needs a particularly good nose for this, but, if vulcanite is kept in an air-tight plastic bag for a few days, the smell of sulphur can be detected more easily when the bag is opened.

Vulcanite does not show a conchoidal fracture, and the small fractures of this type often seen on jet articles help to identify the latter. The fracture of vulcanite is

Figure 7.9 Vulcanite jewellery showing the same cameo head on all three items. Length of necklace, 517 mm, centre pendant, 46 × 65 mm

Figure 7.10 A variety of vulcanite hand brooches. Size of centre brooch, 50 × 50 mm

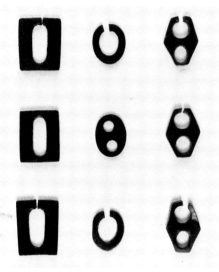

Figure 7.11 Vulcanite chain links and how they open

rough, but because it is tougher than jet very little damage is usually found. Similarly there is no cracking with age. Lack of wear on an old piece is a good indication of its nature.

Vulcanite jewellery is available today in sufficient quantity to make it a profitable collecting field. Because of the large numbers of any one design which were produced, the jewellery can be repetitive and certain designs will be found again and again (*Figure 7.9*). On the other hand it is a truly Victorian product and certain items, such as hand brooches, are very varied and attractive (*Figure 7.10*).

Vulcanite chains (*Figure 7.11*) frequently pose a problem of identification, but in fact they need not do so. Jet chains are made (Chapter 5) with each alternate link solid and alternating links split in *two* places and then pinned and glued together. Because vulcanite is thermoplastic, only one cut is necessary in the chain link which can then be opened when heated and slipped onto the next link and closed again. Thus distinguishing jet from vulcanite chains is merely a question of ascertaining whether the links have one or two joins.

Figure 7.12 A typical vulcanite locket showing the decoration on the inside surface

As mentioned in Chapter 5 vulcanite lockets are invariably highly decorated on the inside (*Figure 7.12*) while jet lockets are plain. Often the decorative motif on the front of the locket, whether it be a cameo head or a bunch of flowers, is a separate piece and is pinned onto the locket. Similarly the pins on vulcanite brooches are usually attached by two screws, while those on jet are glued on. Vulcanite bracelets are sometimes made of a wide piece of flexible plastic with a separate centre piece screwed in place (*Figures 7.9* and *7.13*). Others are made of segments like jet. Because the plastic shrinks very slightly on cooling, the underside of the segments are often concave. All these observations help to identify vulcanite jewellery without the need to resort to any tests.

Figure 7.13 Three vulcanite bracelets. The lower segmented bracelet bears the head of Queen Victoria. Size of cameo centre (T.R.), 43 × 51 mm, solid band of bracelet, 200 mm long

American books on antique jewellery frequently describe articles of gutta percha. This is a natural plastic obtained from the milky secretion of the tree *Dichopsis gutta*. Although rather similar to rubber, it does not become vulcanized by heating with sulphur. Although jewellery was made from gutta percha, as were such items as picture frames and match boxes, very few survive to the present day. Gutta percha was not durable and it is most likely that those pieces of jewellery described as gutta percha are in fact made of vulcanite.

Vulcanite was largely replaced in the 20th century by the new plastic bakelite.

Bakelite

Bakelite is a phenolic resin made from phenol formaldehyde. It was the first truly synthetic plastic. Its inventor, Leo Hendrik Baekeland, patented the formula in 1909. Since it was not available before the 20th century its use as a simulant of jet was not as widespread as that of vulcanite. However, a certain amount of black bakelite jewellery was produced, mostly in the form of brooches, bracelets and beads. If they are plain and round, without faceting or carving, the beads are the most deceptive of these and can pose some difficulty in identification.

Bakelite weighs about as much as jet, has a good deep black colour which does not fade and takes a good polish. When scratched it gives a black powder and a black streak on porcelain. Like other plastics it can be moulded when heated. When burnt or touched with a heated needle it gives a typical smell of phenol (carbolic acid).

Bakelite jewellery is tough and not as readily damaged as jet and thus a too perfect piece may arouse suspicion. With jet beads the drill hole frequently shows very tiny conchoidal fractures. Plastic beads have perfectly round and smooth drill holes. Fortunately much bakelite jewellery other than beads is stamped on the reverse with the word 'patent', making a test unnecessary.

Epoxy resin

The latest plastic to be used for the reproduction of jet jewellery is epoxy resin. One or two museums are making very good imitation copies of their jet pieces using this plastic (*Figure 7.14*). Epoxy resin is thermosetting unlike vulcanite and bakelite which are thermoplastic. The reverse side of these epoxy resin pieces is sometimes concave where the plastic has shrunk when it set.

The museum copies, although never intended to deceive, have often turned up on flea-market stalls being sold as jet. They are originally sold on a card which states that they are copies, but as the cards are thrown away immediately after purchase it would have been desirable for the museum to have stamped the reverse with some indication of the true nature of the copies.

Epoxy resin gives a black powder on scratching and a heated needle applied to the surface produces the smell of carbolic.

Figure 7.14 An epoxy resin copy of a jet cameo of Dante from the Castle Museum York. Size, 46 × 56 mm

Other materials

Other black materials which may superficially resemble jet but which are of little importance since their use was very limited are:

Bois durci

This was patented in France and consists of wood-flour (very fine saw dust) mixed with albumen from either egg or blood and stained with lamp black. It is reputed to have been used to make jewellery between 1850 and 1880, but as it was not very durable examples are rarely seen (Katz, 1984).

Black enamel

This is sometimes found on brooches and rings. Like glass it is harder than jet and cannot be scratched with a pin.

Wood

Some cheap jewellery was made by painting wood with black enamel paint. A scratch reveals the wood beneath the paint.

Onyx and chalcedony

These two natural varieties of quartz occur in black or can be stained black. Onyx was frequently used in Victorian jewellery. There is no need for confusion with jet since all minerals are colder to the touch and much heavier than jet. Quartz, having a hardness of 7 on Mohs' scale, cannot be scratched with a pin.

The identification of jet

The standard gemmological tests are not normally used in the identification of jet. Optical tests are of little value due to its opacity. Jet is said to produce a vague R.I. reading at about 1.66 on the refractometer. Its specific gravity varies within a range which includes many of its simulants.

Identification must therefore be a process of elimination. There is no single infallible test which will distinguish jet from all its natural and man-made imitations. Some very modern technological methods have been used including ultra-sound, infra-red spectroscopy and X-ray analysis, but these are for scientific study and are seldom available to the layman or the average jeweller.

In the end it comes down to observation or very simple destructive tests. Of the latter there are three: the scratch test with a steel pin, the streak test on unglazed porcelain, and either the application of a heated needle or the burning of a small fragment. All these are to a greater or lesser degree destructive and might not be possible on specimens which do not belong to the tester.

Therefore observation with the naked eye and with a 10× lens must play a significant part in identification. Indeed, in the vast majority of cases this is all that is required by the experienced collector.

Observation

1   *Colour*: Although colour is only a rough guide, the phrase 'as black as jet' has not been in use in our language for centuries without very good reason for the colour of jet is a deep and intense black. None of the other coal-type substances are quite as black. Anthracite is the nearest, but it has a brittle appearance while the black of jet is deep and velvety. Cannel coal has a silvery sheen, Kimmeridge shale is rather brown or greyish black and bog oak and horn are more brown than black. As for the man-made simulants, vulcanite has a tendency to fade, but bakelite most nearly approaches jet in its colour.

2   *Heat conductivity*: Because of its low heat conductivity, jet feels warm to the touch, but so do many of its simulants. This test will, however, eliminate the natural stones, onyx and chalcedony, which feel cold because they are relatively good heat conductors. Glass also feels colder than jet but less so than the natural stones.

3   *Electricity*: The ability of jet to become electrically charged when rubbed distinguishes it from coal, cannel coal and bog oak. Many of the plastics, though, have the same property, particularly bakelite.

4   *Weight*: The natural gem stones and glass are heavier than jet and this can be easily determined by hefting. Most of the other simulants vary little from jet in this respect. Specific gravity tests are not of much use because the S.G. of jet itself varies within the range of many of its simulants.

5   *Fracture*: Small conchoidal fractures are typical of jet especially if it is well worn, but they also occur in coal and glass. However, lack of any wear of this type or a different type of fracture is strong contra evidence.

6   *Design*: Since the plastic imitations were moulded they were turned out in large numbers of identical design. This is particularly true of vulcanite, which must have been produced in considerable quantity in the 19th century. For this reason the same design may be encountered time after time and then it becomes instantly recognizable as vulcanite. An example of this is the drop shaped pendant with a beaded border. This sometimes bears a cameo head, and sometimes vines (*Figure 7.7*). Such a design is so common that it can be recognized in a photograph without even handling the original. One well-known book on Victorian jewellery has seven illustrations described as jet which are easily recognizable as vulcanite.

7   *Method of manufacture*: All true jet is hand carved and all the man-made simulants are moulded. This is probably the one most crucial characteristic. Signs of hand carving are the squared off edges to the design, undercutting and a high relief. Moulded articles do not normally show undercutting; they have rounded edges and lower relief. Sometimes plastic jewellery is too highly ornamented. For example the inside of a vulcanite locket is always very attractively decorated under the glass compartment, while that of jet is always plain and unpolished.

Simple tests

1   *The powder and streak tests*: These can be dealt with together as the resulting colours are the same in both cases. A very small scratch with a steel pin in an inconspicuous spot gives two results. First the feel of the material as the pin scratches it is typical. In plastic materials the pin scrapes along smoothly. In jet it is possible to feel the bite and more pressure is needed. Secondly the colour of the powder produced is characteristic. A black powder immediately rules out jet which gives a brown one. A brown powder, however, might also be produced by lignite (of little importance to the jeweller), bog oak (which is identifiable by other means) or vulcanite. The streak test gives the same colours on unglazed porcelain and is less destructive.

2   *The burning test*: A small chip of the material may be removed with a sharp knife and ignited. Since this damages the finished article, the application of a heated needle to an inconspicuous spot is preferable. This is the most conclusive of all tests, but unfortunately can only be performed once the article has been bought. Antique dealers do not as a rule look with favour on customers who stick red-hot needles into their jewellery Yet some will be willing to allow a streak test to be performed.

In most cases mere observation should be sufficient for identification without any further tests being carried out. However, a very small number of articles can be difficult and require careful testing.

Generally speaking it is only the archaeologists who will be confronted with lignite, Kimmeridge shale and cannel coal. Most jewellers or collectors will be more concerned with the plastics and their biggest problem is vulcanite. Because both jet and vulcanite give a brown powder and streak it is usually only for these two that the hot needle test is needed. When that is applied, however, it is quite conclusive – jet gives the unmistakeable smell of a coal fire while vulcanite smells of burning rubber.

If for example one were given an assortment of black beads, the simple heft test would immediately eliminate all the natural black minerals including onyx, chalcedony, black tourmaline and garnet. The typical Irish decoration, coupled with a brown and unpolished appearance, will identify bog oak. Both glass (French jet) and enamel cannot be scratched with a pin. Horn produces a grey powder. Bois durci and painted wood reveal their woody nature when scratched. Bakelite, all the shales and coals give a black powder and streak. Lignite shows a woody structure and is brown in colour. That leaves jet and vulcanite. These may be differentiated if there is evidence of hand carving or moulding, and if that fails then the result of the hot needle test will be conclusive.

References

ANON, *Spon's Encyclopaedia*, Division II, Spon, London (1882)

CALKIN, J. B., 'Kimmeridge coal money', *Proceedings of the Dorset Natural History and Antiquities Society*, **75**, (1953)

CUNLIFFE, B., *Iron age communities in Britain*, Routledge and Kegan Paul, London (1974)

KATZ, S., *Classic Plastics*, Thames and Hudson (1984)

KUNZ, G. F., *Gems and precious stones*, The Scientific Publishing Co., New York (1890)

MARSHALL, C. E., 'The jet age', *Australian Gemmologist*, (1974)

Where to find jet

Most of the beaches where jet can be found present difficulties of access and may be under water at high tide. Before attempting to reach them it is advisable to check the local high tide tables and leave the beach three hours before a high tide is due. The cliffs are very dangerous and rock falls are common; therefore one should always wear a helmet and keep away from overhanging cliffs. If a seam of jet is found, it is best to remove the shale from below the seam and then gently prise the jet away from the shale above, attempting to remove it in large flat pieces.

It is easier and safer to search for jet washed up on the shore where it is usually found around the high tide mark or jammed between the rocks in small pools. Sea coal is also washed up in the same area but this gives a black streak on a piece of unglazed porcelain or on a white pebble. Sea coal is a good indicator – where coal is found jet is often found too.

Most of the old jet mines inland are worked out and are dangerous and should not be entered without an experienced guide, but searching through the old spoil heaps can be rewarding. Most of the mines are on private land so permission must be obtained first.

Finally rough jet can be bought in the shops in Whitby. Unlike other beach pebbles jet cannot be tumbled.

Appendix 2

Working jet

Because of its low hardness, jet is not difficult to work but it is brittle and must be treated with a light touch. Another thing to remember is that jet is a type of coal and if it becomes overheated by friction, as in drilling, it will easily ignite.

The method of working jet used by the 19th century workers has been described in Chapter 4. Today's lapidaries do not usually have access to the lathes and wheels that the Victorians used and simpler methods can be equally effective. Most of the modern workers have their own ideas and vary in their choice of tools and polishes. This, however, is how one of the best of today's craftsmen works his jet and examples of the finished product can be seen in Figure 4.34. This is a description of how he would make a pendant.

First, a suitable piece of rough jet is chosen for its size and thickness. It is then carefully studied for flaws. If the piece has a skin or spar, it is removed with rough emery paper and this will reveal any flaws or inclusions of stone in the jet. If it is clean, the surface is first flattened on a rough emery paper or a sandstone grinder. This is followed by 80 grit emery paper and then 120 grit paper. It helps to wrap the emery paper around a flat piece of wood. Then the shape of the pendant is cut out with a hacksaw. To do this the jet is held firm in a piece of plasticine or mastic blue-tac.

Next it is drilled with a pin vice using a $\frac{1}{16}$ in or $\frac{1}{32}$ in drill for the pilot hole. The pilot hole is reamed out with a $\frac{1}{4}$ in drill to the size required. Drilling is done wet to keep the jet from overheating and if an electric drill is used it must be done very slowly. Then the outer edge of the pendant is smoothed off with a file and 120 emery paper. Finally it is polished with 1000 or 1200 grit wet-and-dry and Brasso or a wax polish to give a high shine.

To inlay a piece of jet with, for example, mother-of-pearl the inlay is cut out with a hacksaw using a templet for the shape. It is then smoothed with emery paper on both sides. Next the mother-of-pearl is glued onto a piece of jet to hold it firmly and the outline is marked firmly with a metal scriber. The inlay is then removed using hot water or steam to dissolve the glue and the outlined shape is cut away with a scalpel. When ready the mother-of-pearl is glued in and the whole thing is rubbed over with very fine emery paper.

Working patterns or milling the jet is done with a triangular, round or flat needle file. Settings, pins etc. can be bought at any lapidary shop and the jet set with an epoxy glue such as rapid araldite.

Whitby jet ornament manufacturers 1849

Agar, George, *Church Street*
Andrew, Thomas, *New Pier*
Bingant, Robert, *Church Street*
Brown, John, *Church Street*
Bryan, George, *Baxtergate*
Clegg, Thomas, *Baxtergate*
Flintoft and Lister, *Church Street*
Greenbury, Isaac, *Baxtergate*
Greenbury, Robert, *Church Street*
Stainthorp, George, *Church Street*
Turnbull, Thomas, *Church Street*

Source: Slater's Commercial Directory of Yorkshire and Lincolnshire (1849)

Whitby jet merchants and ornament manufacturers 1867

Jet merchants

Dale, Edw., *Wellclose Square*
Dobson, Roger, *Spring Hill*
Walker, Cornelius, *Cliff Street*

Jet ornament manufacturers

Allison, Thos., *Henrietta Street*
Anderson, Robert, *Brunswick Street*
Anderson, Wm., *Borough Place*
Andrew, Thomas, *Marine Parade*
Appleby, Thos., *Church Street*
Argument and Harland, *Church Lane*
Baker, Thos., *Bridge Street*
Barry, Wm., *Church Street*
Barton, Aaron, *Church Street*
Bell, Edward, *Church Street*
Bennison, Thomas, *Sander's Yard*
Bowerin, Robert, *Sander's Yard*
Brown, John, *Old Post Office Yard*
Bryan, Charles, *John Street*
Bryan, Thomas, *Springhill*
Busfield, Thos., *Morley's Yard*
Carr, John, *Church Street*
Clegg, John, *Blackburn's Yard*
Clegg, Robert, *Blackburn's Yard*
Clegg, Thomas, *Blackburn's Yard*
Clegg, Thomas, *St. Ann's Staith*
Cole, Robert, *Arundel Place*
Consitt, Robert, *Clarkson Street*

Corner, Edw., *Blackburn's Yard*
Cox, Marshall, *Church Street*
Cox, Robert and William, *Longsteps*
Dillon, Andrew, *Church Street*
Dillon, Richard, *Church Street*
Doughty, Richard, *Pier Land*
Doughty Thomas, *Cliff Street*
Dring, Thomas and George, *Church Street*
Eskdale, Jeremh, *Fawcett's Yard*
Fletcher, Robert, *Church Street*
Fowler, W., *Bowlby Lane*
Frank, Thos., *Sander's Yard*
Frankland, John, *Church Street*
Frankland, Wm., *Church Street*
Garbutt and Warnock, *Church Street*
Greenbury, Edward Heselton, *Marine Parade*
Greenbury, Matthew, *Brunswick Street*
Greenbury, Robert, *Clarance Place*
Greenbury and Wakefield, Baxtergate
Harker, William, *Church Street*
Harland, John, *New Quay*
Harland, Wm., *Church Street*
Harrison, George, *Cuthbert's Yard*
Harrison, John, *Sander's Yard*
Harrison, Wm., *Cliff Street*
Hick, Isaac, *Blackburn's Yard*
Heselton, Stephenson, *Blackburn's Yard*
Hodgman, Thos., *Sander's Yard*
Hogarth, Andrew, *Boulby Bank*
Holman and Kingston, *Sander's Yard*
Huntrod, W., *Burn's Yard*
Hutchinson, Jas., *Elephant and Castle Yard*
Jefferson, George, *Hospital Yard*
Kingston, Thomas, *Sander's Yard*
Knaggs, William, *Skinner Street*
Langley, Bedlington, *Church Street*
Locker, George, *Blackburn's Yard*
Marshall, Brown, *Church Street*
Maule, James Dixon, *Cass Yard*
Mickman, James, *Gas Office Yard*
Midland, John, *Morley's Yard*
Mirfield, Michael, *Blackburn's Yard*
Noble, Edward, *Church Street*
Noble, Henry, *Boulby Bank*
Noble, Mark, *Boulby Bank*
Parratt, Edward, *Brunswick Street*

Parker, Thomas, *Blackburn's Yard*
Pearce, Joseph, *Baxtergate*
Pearson, Christopher, *Morley's Yard*
Raw, Harry, *Baxtergate*
Readman, Joshua, *Sander's Yard*
Readman, Wm., *Wellington Road*
Robinson, Robert, *Church Street*
Ross, John, *Church Street*
Sanderson, James, *Cass Yard*
Slater, David, *Bakehouse Yard*
Speedy, James, *Church Street*
Speedy, George and John, *Cliff Street*
Stewart, Daniel, *Sander's Yard*
Stubbs, John, *Coles Lane*
Swales, Ch., *Church Street*
Thompson, Wm., *Blackburn's Yard*
Tireman, J., *Smith's Yard*
Tose, Robert, *Blackburn's Yard*
Trueman, Chas., *Brunswick Street*
Turnbull Bros., *Bridge Street*
Urwin, Edward, *Gas Office Yard*
Varley, Abraham, *Paddock Street*
Walker, Hy., *Low Hospital Yard*
Whitehead, Wm., *Brunswick Street*
Wood, Abel, *Muncaster's Yard*
Wright, William, *Marine Parade*

Source: White's Directory, North Riding of Yorkshire (1867)

Whitby rough jet merchants and jet ornament manufacturers 1890

Rough jet merchants

Cariss, J. H., *Church Street*
Hall, Thomas, *Baxtergate*
Hopper, George, *Quay Side*
Langdale, I., *Baxtergate*
Larroude, P., *Church Street*
Pearson, C., *Flowergate*
Pearson, W. Robert, *Flowergate*
Peguero, Raymond, *Church Street*
Walker, Elisha, *Boulby Bank*
Wright, Wm., *Marine Parade*

Jet ornament manufacturers

Agar, Wm., *Blacksmith's Arms Yard*
Allison, Thos., *Church Street*
Anderson, Chris, *Haggersgate*
Anderson, Edward, *Grape Lane*
Anderson, Robert, *Mennell's Buildings*
Andrew, Thomas, *Imperial Yard*
Baker, George, *White Horse Yard*
Baker, Thomas, *Routh's Walk*
Ballard, V., *Cappleman's Yard*
Barber, T., *Waterloo Old Yard*
Barry, William, *Tate's Yard*
Bell, Thomas, *Olive Buildings*
Blackstone, Aaron, *Church Street*
Boanas, Rd. Thos., *Church Street*
Boanas, Wm., *Flowergate*
Braithwaite, John, *Cliff Street*
Breckon, Benjamin, *New Quay*

Brown, Hy., *Blackburn's Yard*
Brown T., *Elephant and Castle Yard*
Bryan, Charles, *Well Close Square*
Bryan, Mrs. Margaret, *Baxtergate*
Bryan's (Thomas) Sons, *Princess Place*
Calvert, W., *Primitive Methodist Chapel Yard*
Chapman, W., *Dock End*
Clark, Francis, *Taylorsons Yard*
Coates, John, *Baxtergate*
Cook, T., *Dark Entry, Baxtergate*
Corner, J., *Mennell's Buildings*
Cox, Marshall Salton, *Boulby Bank*
Cox, Robert, *Mennell's Buildings*
Davidson, Henry, *Imperial Yard*
Dawson, William Cooper, *Esk Terrace*
Day, Robert, *Well Close Square*
Dixon, John, *Henrietta Street*
Douthwaite, George, *Paddock*
Elder, Michael, *Henrietta Street*
Elders, Isaac, *Goodwill's Yard*
Eskdale, Jeremiah, *Church Street*
Fenwick Bros., *Boulby Bank*
Feran, Stephan, *Victoria Square*
Fletcher, George, *Church Street*
Fletcher, Mrs. H., *Church Street*
Fletcher, Joseph, *Elbow Yard*
Fletcher, John, *Boulby Bank*
Frankland, Francis, *Primitive Methodist Chapel Yard*
Frankland, W., *Church Street*
Frank, Thos., *Albion Place*
Franks, Alfred, *Wald's Yard*
Freeman, Henry Charles, *Skinner Street*
Gay, Wm., *Saltpanwell Steps*
Gibson, Charles, *Foresters Court*
Gill, James, A., *Golden Lion Bank*
Greenbury, Isaac, *Church Street*
Harker, Wm., *Church Street*
Harland, Francis George, *Smallwood's Buildings*
Harland, George Davidson, *Bagdale*
Harland, William, *Church Street*
Harrison, H. C., *St. Ann's Lane*
Harrison, John, H., *Church Street*
Harrison, Matthew, *Church Street*
Harrison, P., *Taylorson's Yard*
Harrison, Wm., *Frank's Yard*
Hartley, Wm., *Cliff Street*

Haxwell, Thos., *Church Street*
Heselton, George, *Green Lane*
Heselton, R., *Blackburn's Yard*
Hobson, R., *Cappelman's Yard*
Hogman, Thos., *Blacksmith's Arms Yard*
Hodgson, Joseph, *Cliff Street*
Hoggarth Bros., *Blacksmith's Arms Yard*
Hoggarth, John, *Aelfleda Terrace*
Holman, Robert, *George Street*
Holmes, Richard, *Haggersgate*
Hopper, George, *Quay Side*
House, James, *Church Street*
House, Joseph, *Tin Ghaut*
Hutchinson, Matt., *Flowergate*
Hutchinson, T., *Church Street*
Jameson, Thos., *Boulby Bank*
Jefferson, Henry, *High Walk*
Knaggs, John, *Henrietta Street*
Langdale, Isaac, *Steam Mill Buildings, New Quay*
Larroude, P., *Church Street*
Leck, Peter, *Aefleda Terrace*
Leck, Thomas, *Smallwoods Buildings*
Leck, Wm., *Boulby Bank*
Leng, William, *Aelfleda Terrace*
Lorains, Jas., *Henrietta Street*
Love, Hammon, *Baxtergate*
Lythe, T., *Flowergate*
Lund, William, *Henrietta Street*
Marshall, Joseph, *Cliff Street*
McNab, John, *Poplar Row*
Midwood, James, *Borough Place*
Midwood, John, *Boulby Bank*
Noble, Edward, *Church Street*
Noble, Hy., *Smallwood's Buildings*
Noble, Robert. *Henrietta Street*
Page and Young, *Smallwood's Buildings*
Parratt, T. W., *Brunswick Street*
Patton, Peter, *Cliff Street*
Peacock, John, *Henrietta Street*
Pearson and Allison, *Primitive Methodist Chapel Yard*
Pearson, Wm., *Flowergate*
Peart, George, *Church Lane*
Preston, T. and Co., *Flowergate*
Readman, Wm., *Church Street*
Robinson, John, *Aelfleda Terrace*
Roe, Martin, *Cliff Street*

Roe, T., *Bagdale*
Roe, Wm., *Blackburn's Yard*
Ross, Thomas, *Dock End*
Sample, John, *Baxtergate*
Sanderson, Bros., *Flowergate Cross*
Sedman, George, *Baxtergate*
Shaw, John, *Hilda's Terrace*
Shepherdson, Thos., *Primitive Methodist Chapel Yard*
Sherwood, John, *Boulby Bank*
Short, Samuel, *Kiln Yard*
Slater, Joseph, *Imperial Yard*
Snowdon, Matthew, *Brunswick Street*
Speedy, James, *Black Horse Yard*
Stabler, Harry, *Imperial Yard*
Stephenson, R., *Church Street*
Steward, William Henry and John, *Clarence Place*
Stewart, Alfred, *Baxtergate*
Stonehouse, William, *Albion Place*
Storr, Richard, *Church Street*
Stuart, Wm., *Skinner Street*
Sunley, Chris., *Blackburn's Yard*
Swales, Robert, *Miller's Yard*
Thompson, S., *Aelfleda Terrace*
Thompson, Thos., *Boulby Bank*
Thorton, J. T., *Flowergate*
Thornton, Wm. *Imperial Yard*
Thornton, Joseph, *Brunswick Street*
Tose, James William, *Imperial Yard*
Tose, Robert, *Grove Street*
Trattles, M., *Blackburn's Yard*
Trattles, Thos., *Victoria Square and New Quay*
Turnbull Bros., *Flowergate*
Tweedy, George, *Henrietta Street*
Urwin, George, *Grove Street*
Varley, Robert, *Cliff Street*
Waite, John, *Grape Lane*
Walker, Elisha, *Church Street*
Walker, Henry, *Church Street*
Walker, Oswald, *Baxtergate*
Walker, William, *The Cragg*
Webster, Thomas, *Baxtergate*
Wheatley, J. A., *Boulby Bank*
Whitby Jet Association Ltd., *St. Ann's Staith*
Whitby Jet Co., *Flowergate*
White, Wm., *1st Hospital Yard*
Wilson, T., *Royal Crescent*

Winterburn, F. R., *Silver Street*
Wood, George, *Boulby Bank*
Wood, Jas., *Brunswick Street*
Wood, John Thos., *Smallwood's Buildings*
Wren, Thos., *St. Hilda's Cottage*
Wren, Walter, *Baxtergate*
Wright Bros., *Imperial Yard*
Wright, William, *Marine Parade*
Young, Charles

Source: History topography and Directory of North Yorkshire, Bulmer T. (1890)

Whitby jet manufacturers and workers 1905

Jet manufacturers

Pearson, William, *Flowergate*

Jet ornament manufacturers

Gale, T., *Church Street*
Gill, J. A., *Golden Lion Bank*
Harland, George Davison, *Bagdale*
Hodgman, John. H., *Church Street*
Hodgman, Thomas, *Church Street*
Parratt, T. W. & Son., *Brunswick Street*
Preston, T. & Co., *Flowergate*
Reid, John, *Marine Parade*
Sample, John, *Baxtergate*
Storr, Richard, *Church Street*
Turnbull Bros., *Flowergate*
Walker, E., *Church Street*
Wren, Thomas, *Abbey Plain*

Jet ornament workers

Cox, M., *Elbow Yard*
Harrison, George, *Newholm*
Headlam, John, *Falcon Terrace*
Pearson, William, R., *Flowergate*
Ross and Chapman, *Haggersgate*
Stonehouse, Wm., *Albion Place*
Thompson, Snowdon, *Aelfleda Terrace*
Tompson, Thomas, *Smales Gallery*
Trattles, Thomas, *West Hill*

Source: Kelly's Directory of the North and East Ridings of Yorkshire (1905)

Index